JESUS

THE MOST INFLUENTIAL LIFE EVER LIVED

Dr. Elmer Towns' vivid description of the Gospel accounts makes you feel like you are actually there alongside the Lord Jesus Himself. Highly recommended.

BILL BRIGHT (1921–2003)
Founder, Campus Crusade for Christ International
Orlando, Florida

We believe this historical novel on the life of Jesus has the potential of leading many people to Him. The author's easy-to-read style makes this book ideal as a family devotional. We heartily endorse *Jesus: The Most Influential Life Ever Lived.*

DAVID AND GRACE CHO
Founder, Yoido Full Gospel Church
Seoul, Korea

Every married couple has a responsibility to communicate the story of the Savior to their kids and grandkids. *Jesus: The Most Influential Life Ever Lived* is a warm, human, "this-is-real" way to share this rich treasure with your family.

JACK AND ANNA HAYFORD
Chancellor, The King's University, Los Angeles
Founder, The Church On The Way

Jesus: The Most Influential Life Ever Lived is an approach to the gospel that carries me and my wife, Anne, back to the days when we first shared the greatest story ever told with our daughter Jennifer in the early days of our ministry. How precious are these immortal stories of our Lord as He dwelt among humankind! Elmer Towns' narrative is easy to read and faithful to the details of Scripture. Excellent family reading!

D. JAMES KENNEDY (1930–2007)
Founder, Coral Ridge Presbyterian Church
Fort Lauderdale, Florida

A unique and fascinating presentation of the life of our Lord by a man who can always be counted on to be faithful to the Scriptures, *Jesus: The Most Influential Life Ever Lived* makes for enjoyable reading of the greatest story ever told!

TIM LA HAYE
Coauthor, *Left Behind* Series and *Soul Harvest*
Rancho Mirage, California

The life and times of the most important figure in all of history have been beautifully rendered in this compelling masterwork. Elmer Towns has realized the life of Christ as a grand adventure that amuses and entertains even as it uplifts and inspires. *Jesus: The Most Influential Life Ever Lived* is a book for the ages.

ROBERT H. SCHULLER
Founder, Crystal Cathedral Ministries
Garden Grove, California

HE WAS SENT TO SAVE THE WORLD

JESUS

THE MOST INFLUENTIAL LIFE EVER LIVED

ELMER L. TOWNS

Jesus: The Most Influential Life Ever Lived by Elmer L. Towns
Originally published as *The Son* by Regal Books in 1999.
ISBN 0-8307-2428-1

This condensed version was printed by
Guideposts Condensed Books in 2006.

ISBN 978-0-7684-1007-5

Cover and Interior Design by
InsideOut Design, rob.insideoutdesign@cox.net

Considering all the teachers of all the ages . . . Jesus has influenced far more lives, for people to learn far more knowledge, about far more things; than any other instructor of the ages.

Considering all the writers of all the ages . . . Jesus has motivated far more literature, about far more subjects, to teach far more knowledge, to lift people far higher; than any other authors of the ages.

Considering all the workmen of all the ages . . . Jesus is responsible for far more construction, of far more different kinds of buildings, to help far more people, in far more different ways; than any other carpenter of the ages.

Considering all the social workers of all the ages . . . Jesus has help raise far more money, to give far more help, to far more needy; than any other humanitarian of the ages.

Considering all the artists of all the ages . . . Jesus has breathed far more life into far more paintings, sculptures and art works, and to uplift far more people, to far more higher levels of aspiration; than any other artist of the ages.

Considering all the politicians and statesmen of all ages . . . Jesus is responsible for far more good, to far more subjects, in far more areas of their life; than any other ruler of the ages.

Considering all the military personnel that have ever defended freedom, Jesus has motivated far more to defend freedom for all people, for far more people; and to attack more different kinds of evil; than any defender of the ages.

Considering all the individuals ever born, Jesus Christ is the greatest influence to ever live.

Elmer Towns

P.S. This is an historical novel of Jesus Christ, based on the records found in the Bible. It's written to help you know Jesus and believe in Him. As you reach out to touch Him, you will find He'll reach to touch you.

AND THE WORD WAS WITH GOD,

AND THE WORD WAS GOD.

ALL THINGS WERE MADE THROUGH HIM,

AND WITHOUT HIM NOTHING WAS MADE

THAT WAS MADE. IN HIM WAS LIFE,

AND THE LIFE WAS THE LIGHT OF MEN.

AND THE WORD BECAME FLESH AND DWELT

AMONG US, AND WE BEHELD HIS GLORY,

THE GLORY AS OF THE ONLY BEGOTTEN OF

THE FATHER, FULL OF GRACE AND TRUTH.

HE WAS IN THE WORLD, AND THE WORLD WAS

MADE THROUGH HIM, BUT THE WORLD

DID NOT KNOW HIM. HE CAME TO HIS OWN,

AND HIS OWN DID NOT RECEIVE HIM.

CHAPTER 1

The old man looked wistfully to the distant mountains. The leathery skin stretched over his frail bones told that he was past sixty years of age. He looked for Messiah to come each day—the one who would deliver his people from Rome's oppression. But the Messiah had not come.

"Come inside to eat." His elderly wife stood at the door of their home in Abia, a community that was home to Jerusalem's priests.

"I'm not hungry . . . ."

"Not hungry? Is it because of joy . . . or sadness?"

Zechariah smiled. Tomorrow would be his last day of Temple duty. He was retiring. Tomorrow, when he entered the Holy Room to offer evening prayers, it would be his first—and last—time to pray for his nation. Priestly duties were assigned by lottery, and a priest could have the privilege of burning incense in the Holy Place only once in his lifetime—sometimes never. If the selection had not been made for tomorrow, Zechariah would have ended his service . . . unfulfilled.

"Don't frown," his wife, Elizabeth, told Zechariah. "You'll do fine."

Zechariah was not worried about praying.

"I'm concerned about the younger priests," he told his wife. "They do not love people, they love power. They have lost their faith."

"And why not?" Elizabeth wondered. "What is there to have faith in?"

"Hush!" Zechariah protested. "We must have faith in the Word of God—not look for miracles."

"I do. I *do*," Elizabeth declared. "But where *is* God? If the Almighty One loves his people, why doesn't he send Messiah to drive the Romans into the sea?"

Excitement swept Zechariah and Elizabeth along the path on their short walk to Jerusalem the next day. Friends and family accompanied them.

They entered the Temple, and Zechariah reached out to rub the gold on its gate one last time in his official role as a priest. Inside he glimpsed the twelve golden stairs and on a platform the Levitical choir.

Behind the choir were twelve more golden stairs. Clusters of people milled about, beginning to fill the large courtyards of the Temple.

The priest in the pinnacle measured the falling shadow on the sundial, and when it was four o'clock, he put a trumpet to his lips and sounded the call for prayers. When the last note finished, the choir began to sing.

Zechariah began to climb the golden stairs toward the Holy Room. Supportive eyes watched him disappear between its heavy curtains.

Zechariah stood before the Lord. He bowed his head in gratitude. *I'm going to pray for myself, before I pray for Israel*, he thought. "Lord . . . give me a son."

He didn't mean to ask for a child—he blurted out the words without thinking. It was a prayer he had uttered many times. Elizabeth, his wife, was barren.

Zechariah shivered suddenly. There before him was a beautiful young man.

"Fear not," the young man said. "I am Gabriel. God wants you to know your prayers have been heard. Your wife will become pregnant and deliver a son."

"No!" the old priest protested. "We are too old for children."

"Your son will be special," Gabriel continued. "He will announce the Deliverer of Israel."

"The Messiah is coming?" Zechariah's eyes lit up.

"Your son will not be Messiah," the angel explained, "but your son will prepare the people for his coming."

"But I'm too old," Zechariah protested again.

Gabriel paid no attention. "Your son will have the name John," he instructed.

"Can you prove this?" Zechariah sputtered. "How will I know?"

"You will be unable to speak until the child is born because you did not believe the words of God." Gabriel pointed with an outstretched finger to Zechariah's mouth.

"Ugh . . . ugh . . . ugh . . . ." Nothing came out of Zechariah's mouth.

Forgive me . . . forgive me, Zechariah prayed silently. Then the old man crumpled to the floor.

The priest had been in the Holy Place much longer than was usual. The crowd of worshipers was becoming restless. The priests knew they couldn't enter the Holy Room, but they had to do something. The sun was setting, and the blessing hadn't been given.

A priest spoke to quiet the crowd. "Be patient . . . he will come out soon."

The curtains rippled. Zechariah stepped out onto the stairs.

"Give the benediction!" one of the clerics called.

Zechariah shook his head and pointed to his mouth. "Ugh . . . ugh . . . ugh . . . ." were the only sounds he could make.

The archpriest, sensing trouble, stepped beside his old friend. Lifting his hand, he said to the people, "The Lord bless and keep you. The Lord make his face to shine upon you. The Lord lift up his countenance upon you and give you peace."

CHAPTER **2**

Mary was a pretty young woman, nearly always adorned with a smile. But today she wore a worried look as she walked toward the Nazareth synagogue. Joseph was posting banns for their marriage.

"Suppose the elders say no?" Mary asked her mother.

"They will approve," she assured her anxious daughter. Mary and her mother climbed the outside stairs to the synagogue loft where the women and children sat. They positioned themselves where they could see the elders when Joseph approached.

"They *must* give approval to Joseph," Mary whispered to her mother.

Her mother only smiled. The people in the community knew that Mary was the most godly young woman in the synagogue. When Mary had caught Joseph's eye, the old grandmothers approved. They knew Joseph was a godly young man too.

Joseph rose and handed the parchment to the ruling elder. The elder nodded.

Mary watched without blinking from the balcony. The elders, arranged in a row, were ready to make the announcement. Normally, the old men frowned when young men asked permission to marry. But for Joseph, their wrinkled, old eyes twinkled, their gray beards nodding up and down in approval.

After dinner, Mary rushed to the fig tree to pray. She loved to talk with God.

O Lord God, may your kingdom come in our village, in our family, in my life . . . .

Suddenly, she felt the presence of someone. Pivoting, she saw a stranger.

"Greetings," said the pleasant young man, smiling. "You who are highly favored, the Lord is with you."

Mary gasped. "Who are you?"

"Gabriel," the young man answered. "My name is Gabriel. Do not be afraid," he said. "You have found favor with God. You are to have a child. Your son shall be conceived in your womb, and when he is born, you shall give him the name Jesus."

Mary's heart leaped. In Hebrew, the language of her people, the name Jesus translated to Joshua, meaning "Jehovah saves." A little boy named Jesus would call to mind Joshua, the great leader who had defeated Israel's enemies.

Gabriel interrupted her thoughts. "God shall give your son the throne of his father, David. And his kingdom shall never end."

The Deliverer? Mary thought. *My son will be the Messiah?* The coming of the Messiah had been foretold for hundreds of years. According to the prophecies, Mary was from the right family, descended from David. Her son could defeat the Romans just as the boy David had defeated Goliath, the Philistine giant.

She said to the angel, "I am not yet married to Joseph."

"Joseph is not to be the father," the angel told Mary. "The Holy Spirit shall come upon you and overshadow you, and the child shall be the Son of God."

Mary's thoughts tumbled one over another. *How could she have a child without a father? What would people think? And what of Joseph?*

As though he could read her thoughts, the angel reassured Mary. "Your cousin Elizabeth is too old to have children," he said. "She was said to be barren, but she has conceived. With God nothing is impossible."

Mary struggled briefly, but then she bowed her head. "Behold, Lord," she submitted, "I will be your handmaiden. Do to me what you have promised."

When she opened her eyes again, Gabriel was not there.

CHAPTER **3**

Mary walked up the rough-hewn path toward the village of Abia. She was sixty miles from home. Within her body was a human being, placed there by God.

"Maybe it is best if I stay with Elizabeth for a while," she had told her mother, concerned about what people in Nazareth would say.

Mary approached Elizabeth and Zechariah's house and stood for a moment in front of the open door. Then she walked into the room.

"Hello . . . I am Mary of Nazareth."

"Oh . . . oh . . . oh . . . !" Elizabeth cried out, reaching for her midsection. "My baby just leaped in my womb!"

Then all at once Elizabeth knew. She exclaimed loudly to her uninvited guest, "Blessed are you among women, and blessed is the fruit of your womb!"

At the sound of Mary's voice, the baby in Elizabeth's womb had leaped for joy. Somehow, her unborn baby had recognized the presence of the Messiah. "Why has the mother of our Lord come to see me?" she asked.

But Mary couldn't give an earthly answer. She lifted her voice and praised God:

My soul magnifies the Lord,
And my spirit has rejoiced in God my Savior.
For he has regarded the lowly state of his maidservant.
From this day forward, all generations will call me blessed.

Elizabeth and Mary talked until late in the evening. All that Elizabeth had learned about living with a man of God was absorbed by young Mary.

"What about Joseph?" Elizabeth asked. "W
think?"

Mary admitted that Joseph had at first
their betrothal. But before he could gather tl
nesses, an angel of the Lord appeared to Joseph in a dream.
He had instructed Joseph to take Mary as his wife and to call
the baby Jesus.

CHAPTER **4**

Zechariah sat with friends on the bench in front of his dwelling.
He could hear the moans of Elizabeth from inside. *Lord, make
this delivery easy*, was all he could think of to pray. Then Zechariah
heard the wail of new life: "Wa-a-ah . . . Wa-aah . . . Wa-a-ah!"

The neighbors heard the cry and came running.

"It's a boy!" the midwife announced as she emerged from
the house.

A cheer went up from the crowd gathering in Zechariah's
yard.

Eight days later, the ceremony to circumcise the baby was held.

"Call the baby Zechariah," an uncle announced when the
deed was done.

"Yes! Zechariah," the relatives agreed. "Call the baby
Zechariah."

Zechariah jumped to his feet and waved his arms in protest.
"Ugh . . . ugh . . . ugh . . . ."

He reached for the slate and chalk. The boisterous crowd
grew silent. With shaking hand, Zechariah wrote in large bold
letters: *HIS NAME IS JOHN.*

At the moment Zechariah finished writing, he felt something in his throat. He rubbed his neck with both hands, then

ied to say something. He looked at the words he had written and read aloud. "His name is John."

 ## CHAPTER **5**

"I could have made the trip without the donkey." The petite but very pregnant girl shut her eyes to the pain. "We can't afford this animal."

"The price is not important," replied her young husband. They had taken a shortcut from Jerusalem to Bethlehem and were trying to find a place to sleep before nightfall.

Bethlehem was the home of Mary's parents, and the Roman authorities had commanded everyone to return to his hometown to register for a census.

"Oh!" Mary clutched her midsection. "It's a labor pain."

"Hold on," Joseph counseled. "Count the time between the pains."

Joseph was frantic as he banged at the wooden door. Mary pulled her cloak tighter against the wind. Her labor pains were closer together with every inn that turned them away. Bethlehem was swamped with pilgrims who had returned home for Rome's census.

"No room in this inn!" came a gruff voice from behind the door.

"We've got to have a place! My wife's having labor pains . . . a baby's coming!"

The innkeeper stepped out, closing the door behind him. Providentially, a pain hit and Mary moaned.

The innkeeper flinched. "There," he pointed to the stable. "You can deliver your baby in there."

"Thank you," was all Joseph could say as he led the donkey off.

He found some fresh hay for Mary to lie on, then he found some clean, white cloth. He prepared everything, then sat beside Mary to wait.

Two hours later, it happened—a healthy baby boy was born. Joseph didn't have to swat him. The baby's red face let out a bawl.

"Don't cry, Jesus," the new mother reached for her son. Baby Jesus nestled into Mary's loving arms.

CHAPTER **6**

"The breeze has died down," the shepherd whispered to his younger companion. The shepherds had taken shelter from the wind among low, flat rocks. Several were already sleeping—waiting for their watch.

"Nothing happens this early in the evening," the younger shepherd moaned. His body was cold, his mind was cold, his world was cold.

"When nothing happens," the older shepherd said impatiently, "maybe we'll have peace." He had lost faith in God. The only thing he believed in was the tyranny of Rome.

"When the Deliverer, the Son of David, comes, we'll have peace," said the younger man.

"Ha!" snorted the older shepherd. "Then I can go home, rather than hide up here in the hills." He paused, scratched his beard, and thought of a crime he committed when he was young. Hardened by years of running from the Roman authorities, he had finally taken work as a shepherd to hide.

The younger shepherd had prayed for the Messiah, but for a different reason. He had sinned against his family and village, against God.

"When the Savior comes," the young man broke the silence, "He will purify my memory."

"What is *that* supposed to mean?" the older voice barked.

"I've done something. I try to forget, but I can't."

A warm wind flushed the shepherds' faces. Then the night exploded in LIGHT!

Light from the heavens obliterated the darkness, blinding the two shepherds. With their hearts in their throats and their eyes stinging, they hid their faces.

"Do not be afraid," came a voice.

"Wh-wh-what is it?" the young shepherd managed to ask.

"The voice is from heaven. Only heaven can be this bright," the older shepherd managed to say.

The younger shepherd shouted, "I see people in the sky!"

The older man squinted toward the heavens. The glorious light appeared to be emanating from a breach in the sky. And flooding through the opening were angels. Thousands upon thousands of angels. And they were singing.

"Look . . . look . . . ! There are so many I can't count them!" the youth cried.

"Do not be afraid," the voice behind the light repeated. "I have come to bring you tidings of great joy. Your Savior was born tonight in Bethlehem. He is Christ the Lord."

Then a magnificent sound flooded the night—a sound that flooded out the noise of past failures. The heavenly host praised God, singing: "Glory to God in the highest, and on earth peace, goodwill toward men!"

Then just as suddenly as the angels came, they were gone.

"Let's go!" The younger shepherd leaped to his feet.

"Where?" the others asked.

"Bethlehem! Didn't you hear? The Savior is in Bethlehem." The shepherd in charge now spoke up. "We must bring the Savior a gift. A lamb."

"Mine," the young shepherd volunteered. "My lamb for the baby Savior."

Joseph bolted upright when he heard the noises. Creeping to the door, he tried to be silent.

"Who is there?" Joseph spoke into the dark courtyard.

"We are shepherds," the lead shepherd replied. "Was a baby born here tonight?"

"Yes."

"We must see him. We have been told the child is from God." Joseph opened the stable door wider. "Mary," he whispered. "Some shepherds want to see Jesus."

At Joseph's behest, the shepherds crowded through the door. But when the light shone upon the baby, the shepherds prostrated themselves in adoration.

Several minutes passed as the shepherds worshiped. Then one of them lifted his head and repeated the angels' song: "Glory to God in the highest, and on earth peace, goodwill toward men!"

As one by one the shepherds looked up at the baby, Mary saw their eyes were streaked with tears.

The young shepherd whose secret sin had brought him to this place rose, the spotless lamb in his arms. He approached the feed trough where Jesus lay sleeping. Placing the lamb in the straw, he said simply, "For you. This lamb is in my place."

CHAPTER **7**

"This house is wonderful," Mary chirped as she tidied the table.

Joseph had helped furnish several homes for the residents of Nazareth, but he had done some of his best work here in Bethlehem for his wife and son.

"This house will do for a while," he said, continuing his work. Mary and Joseph had chosen not to return to their hometown of Nazareth, because the rumors there made them uncomfortable.

They remained in Bethlehem, the birthplace of their son. "We'll be close to the Temple for the baby," Joseph had reasoned.

"If Jesus is to be the leader of our nation, he should live near the City of God."

Mary had opened both doors to allow the cool morning air to ventilate the house. Joseph sat on a stool in the corner, carving.

"Look at the camels!" a small boy yelled outside their door.

Mary gathered Jesus in her arms, and she and Joseph stepped into the street, blinking against the sunlight. A large crowd of villagers were gathered about a string of camels.

The lead camel driver was talking to Melki, the boy with the loud voice. The local youth lifted his arm and pointed toward Joseph. Now all eyes stared at Joseph and Mary—and the baby.

A man in a gold turban whispered to a servant, and the servant ran toward Joseph.

Joseph spoke quietly to Mary. "Go in the house," he said. She obeyed.

The servant bowed to Joseph. "We are searching for the one born king of the Jews."

How do they know? Joseph thought before answering. *What do they know?*

Sensing Joseph's apprehension, the servant again bowed deeply. Joseph recognized the curled toes on the man's sandals as a Persian fashion.

"May we visit the young king this evening?" the servant asked.

Joseph again nodded. He was almost too shocked to speak.

Young Jesus sat under the meal table playing quietly. As the twilight faded, the toddler grew tired. Mary lit all the candles they had in the house and sat down for the first time that evening. Jesus crawled into her lap and dozed in her arms.

"THEY'RE COMING!" Joseph heard Melki yelling from down the street. Moments later there came a rapping at the door. Opening it, Joseph was greeted by the sight of a massive camel. The driver beat a stick on the camel's knee, and it knelt.

The servant who had spoken with Joseph earlier bowed. "Why did they ride?" Joseph asked. "It's a short distance from your camp.

"Royalty does not walk in dirty streets," the servant said. With the tapestry robe held in one hand, the camel rider stepped onto the rug. He walked halfway to the house, then turning, snapped his fingers. Two servants lifted a heavy chest and followed him into the house. The second and third camels dislodged their distinguished riders in equally elegant fashion. "We have come to worship the king of the Jews," the first and eldest of the noblemen spoke in flawless Greek.

The other two noblemen strained forward to see the child.

Jesus let out a yawn, and they smiled when they saw it.

"We study the stars," the first nobleman explained. "The stars tell us God has sent a Savior." He said they were called *magi*, or wise men, because their lives were dedicated to studying the scrolls of the ancients.

"How did you know where to find us?" Joseph asked.

"We studied the holy books of the Jews. Your Scriptures promise a Deliverer, saying he will come from among the Jews."

"We believe this to be true," another of the magi spoke up.

"Your Scriptures tell of a star that will be a sign of his birth, so we began searching the sky for his star. About a year ago, a star that had not been in our sky just . . . appeared."

"*His* star," the third wise man insisted.

Jesus slept, blissfully unaware.

"His star began moving; we followed," the wise man's eyes flashed. "The star moved. We obeyed its direction. When we arrived in Jerusalem, we went immediately to see the one called Herod the Great to inquire of this child."

Joseph listened carefully as the wise men described Herod as a fat, arrogant, greedy man.

"I AM THE ONLY KING OF THE JEWS!" Herod had blustered, and demanded they tell him where the boy king could be found.

"We do not know," was their response. "We followed only the star."

"Go then," Herod had told the wise men. "Find him and bring me the location . . . I will come to worship the child."

Joseph's brow furrowed. Herod was ruthlessly cruel. An unsettling fear lodged in the mind of the young father.

The wise old leader clapped his hands for his valet. A cedar chest was placed on the floor before Mary and the child. Bending, the old man opened the chest. All present saw the light from the candle flames flicker off the gold coins inside it.

"Bless the Lord, O my soul," the wise man prayed in the Hebrew tongue.

Another of the magi then brought an expensive flask filled with myrrh, a rare, aromatic sap, and the third dignitary set a cask of frankincense before Mary. He opened the top and released the fragrance into the room.

After a time, the three magi arose. The oldest glanced to his traveling companions for approval, then he asked, "May we get a closer look . . . ? We want to learn his features."

Mary unfolded the cloth from the child's face, then smiled at their guests.

CHAPTER **8**

Mary and Jesus slept peacefully. The town of Bethlehem dozed beneath a blanket of stars. A dog barked in the distance, then let out a whimper. Joseph was awake, but it was not the dog that had roused him. He had been startled out of sleep by a dream.

He was working on a table, growing frustrated with his inability to balance the table's three legs. So he set it aside and instead put the finishing touches on a cradle he had fashioned for the royal family. He stood back to admire his handiwork and realized he had mistakenly made not a cradle, but a feed trough! Terror gripped his heart as a long shadow fell across the doorway. Had the king come for his cradle?

He turned to greet his highness, but it was not the king. There stood a beautiful, but familiar figure, who towered above everything.

"Get up, Joseph," the visitor warned. "An enemy is coming to kill the child. "

Then Joseph knew. This was the messenger who had foretold the birth of Jesus.

"Hurry," the angel warned. "Death comes after sunup. Go to Egypt. Take the child and his mother and stay until I tell you;" the angel said. Joseph nodded his willingness to obey.

There was a faint light in the east when Joseph led Mary out to the donkey. He helped her up, then brought her the bundled child. He threw two sacks filled with gold, frankincense and myrrh over the animal, then tied them. By the time they made their way out of Bethlehem, the light was beginning to reveal the road ahead.

A few miles out of Bethlehem the donkey refused to go any farther, jerking his head angrily against Joseph's direction. The donkey pulled Joseph toward a little stream at the side of the road.

"What's wrong?" Mary was concerned.

"We left so quickly. I didn't give him water."

Mary decided it was a good time to feed Jesus and found a secluded spot out of the breeze. Joseph led the animal into the stream to drink.

Moments later, he heard shouts coming from the direction of Jerusalem. Then Joseph heard the unmistakable tramp of Roman soldiers.

"Stay hidden in the rocks," Joseph instructed his wife.

The troops were led by a centurion dressed in battle gear. Spotting the stream, he stopped to give his horse a drink. The horse waded into the shallow water near the rocks where mother and child were hidden.

Mary prayed, *Lord, don't let Jesus cry.* The toddler closed his eyes and slept.

In the darkness, the Roman officer couldn't see into the bushes, but Joseph could see the centurion clearly enough. He wanted to run, but held his ground. The donkey stood silently.

The centurion jerked at his reins and the white horse ascended the bank from the stream and took up its trot beside the soldiers. With hands on their swords and death on their minds, they marched toward Bethlehem.

Quickly Joseph and Mary were back on the road. By midmorning, they had traveled far enough that their fears subsided.

Three nights later they were halfway to Egypt, and stopped for the night at an oasis. They were almost ready to go to sleep when a gruff voice was heard approaching.

The burly new arrival dropped his pack. Sticking his feet into the cool water, he complained of walking all day to anyone who would listen.

"I never want to see another Jew!" the voice carried over the water. "Yesterday, King Herod killed all the baby boys in Bethlehem!" The traveler went on to describe how the Roman soldiers had stacked the bodies of the babies near the well. Herod had ordered the death of all male children two years old and younger because of a rumor that a rival to his throne had been born in Bethlehem.

Mary looked at Joseph through the evening shadows. She silently wondered, *Why was our Jesus saved?*

 CHAPTER **9**

Mary and Joseph had settled in a small Egyptian town. Joseph worked in a carpenter shop, making furniture for Egyptian customers.

One night a sudden gust of wind blew through the room and Joseph awoke in the darkness. A rooster had crowed, but dawn was not near. He prayed, *Lord, what are you trying to say to me?*

Joseph listened, but nothing came to him and he soon drifted off.

He was back in his shop in Bethlehem, working on the table . . . again. Two years, and he had been unable to balance the three legs. Then his young son entered the shop. Little Jesus walked over to the table and, taking a saw in his small hand, shortened the errant leg. He stepped away and looked at his father for approval.

Joseph nudged the table, but it no longer wobbled. He turned to Jesus. "How did you do this, my son?"

Jesus smiled again and said, "I must be about my father's business. "He then looked past Joseph toward the door. There, towering above the doorway once again, was the messenger of God.

The visitor spoke. "Take Jesus and his mother and return to the land of Israel. Herod is dead."

During the next few days, Joseph wrapped up his business. On the appointed day, the family left Egypt, never to return. Three days later they stopped at the same oasis where they had spent the night on their flight from Bethlehem. That night Joseph lay on his pallet. He soon slipped into sleep and dreamed.

The angel once again visited his shop.

"Do not go to Jerusalem," the angel said to Joseph. "There is danger waiting there for Jesus. Return to Galilee."

Joseph thought about Galilee. They had fled because of the rumors. He was afraid they would criticize Mary. Then Joseph realized all that faced them in Nazareth was embarrassment. In Jerusalem, his son faced death. "It will be as you say, "he told the messenger. "I will return to Nazareth."

CHAPTER **10**

Mary and Joseph had lived in Nazareth for three years. Near the back of the house, Joseph had built a carpenter shop. Mary was pregnant with their third child. She called her son into the house.

"Jesus, it is time to learn how to write." Mary handed him a stylus. "Hold this pen between your fingers like this."

Within a year, he was copying his favorite psalms. "Jesus, if you're going to be a king," Mary would say to him, "then you must write a complete copy of the Scriptures, just like a king. Then the thoughts of Scripture will belong to you."

So each day Jesus copied a different psalm and memorized it, repeating it flawlessly to his mother.

 CHAPTER **11**

"Look, Mary!" Joseph called to his wife. "I always get a thrill when I first see the Eternal City set high on Mount Zion."

Mary and Joseph had left home three days earlier from Nazareth with a caravan of family and friends. The annual pilgrimage to Jerusalem for the Passover was a festive occasion.

Joseph and Mary were taking their twelve-year-old son, Jesus, for his first visit to the Temple. Jesus was now of an age to observe the requirements of Jewish law, and the Law required that Jewish men attend the feasts of Passover, Pentecost and Tabernacles in Jerusalem.

Jesus scooted up the path ahead of his parents toward Jerusalem. He seemed pulled to the city.

Hastening through the crowded corridors of the city the next day, the family entered the Temple. The clamor of the streets died away and the sweet peace of the psalms rippled through the courtyard. Suddenly Jesus dropped to his knees beside Joseph. This experience had been a long time coming, and Jesus wanted to drink deeply from it.

Without coaxing, his childlike voice blended with the resonant sounds of mature priests as they repeated, "Hear, O Israel:

The Lord our God is one Lord! You shall love the Lord with all your heart, with all your soul and strength."

CHAPTER **12**

The family had left Jerusalem at noon for the return home to Nazareth. Walking half a day, they reached El Birech, an oasis north of Jerusalem.

"We'll set up camp over there," Joseph pointed to a grassy place. He nodded to his son James. "Find your brother Jesus and gather some sticks for a fire."

"I can't find Jesus," James said when he returned.

Mary's heart jumped. "Run up ahead and check the campsites," Joseph commanded James. "Ask if they have seen Jesus."

Joseph left the oasis and began retracing their route from Jerusalem, asking anyone he met along the way about Jesus. James returned and reported that no one had seen Jesus all day.

Evening was darkening when Joseph returned to camp. He had not found his son. "Pack up everything," he barked to the younger children. "Jesus must still be in Jerusalem."

Within minutes, the family was back on the road.

By the next day, the parents were frantic. Joseph and Mary knew that Jesus could take care of himself in Nazareth, but this was the city. They were at their wits' end.

Then Joseph remembered the strange look on his son's face when they worshiped at the Temple. "Let's look in the Temple," Joseph said. They hurried to the Temple, and Joseph managed to ask the first priest he saw, "Have you seen a young boy here? Beautiful olive skin? A child's white tunic, well-washed but worn?"

"All the children here look like that," the kindly priest laughed. "But there is a child sitting with the teachers of the Law; he's causing quite a commotion."

Joseph and Mary didn't wait for him to elaborate. Dashing into a courtyard, they saw a tightly grouped crowd of people. There at the center was Jesus, standing in the midst of several bearded teachers and scholars.

"Let me put this question to you . . . ." Jesus directed a question to the scholars. They were sitting at his feet!

Mary could not contain herself any longer. With a voice of concern mixed with relief, she called out, "Son! Why have you worried us?"

The crowd was silent. No one dared speak.

"We have searched all of Jerusalem for you . . . . Mary said. Twelve-year-old Jesus sensed anguish in his mother's voice. "Why didn't you look first in my Father's house?" he asked. "Didn't you know that I would be about my Father's business?"

 CHAPTER **1 3**

Jesus carefully sawed the board, then nailed it into the empty space on the chest he was making. His unerring eye had helped him become an excellent cabinetmaker. His thoughts were interrupted by a scream from the street.

"HELP!"

Jesus rushed from the shop amid cries from the neighbors. The commotion centered on an oxcart with a broken wheel. A crying boy lay pinned beneath.

"My boy!" a terrified mother shrieked.

Two older men grabbed the wagon, but were unable to lift the burden off the lad.

"MOVE!" Jesus commanded his elders. Putting his shoulder under the wagon, he began to strain at the load. Jesus' back muscles rippled under his workman's tunic as the wagon slowly lifted. The older men quickly pulled the boy to safety and into the arms of his weeping mother.

"Jesus," the mother sobbed, "you saved my son."

Jesus tousled the boy's hair. He had done what anyone with his strength would have done. His strength came from working with wood and from digging limestone from a small rock quarry for the homes he and his brothers built.

A few years earlier his father Joseph had died. These days, Jesus supervised the family business, guiding his half-brothers James, Joseph, Simon and Judah in their daily tasks.

Every Sabbath, Jesus was to be found in his favorite seat in the synagogue. When he read from the Law, his diction was clear, his pronunciation flawless.

"Jesus ought to be a rabbi," the women of Nazareth said. Many believed he should study in Jerusalem.

"Too bad Joseph died," the elders had been known to say. "Jesus could have been a great doctor of the law. But the family business. . . ."

As a young businessman in a boisterous community, Jesus was liked and admired by all. He listened to the troubles of his customers and sympathized with neighbors when they lost a loved one. He agonized when he heard of Roman soldiers beating people as they collected taxes. The day was coming when he would lay aside his carpenter's tools and minister to people with hurts like those he witnessed every day.

One day, word came that a prophet of God was preaching repentance and baptizing people in the Jordan River. Multitudes were flocking to hear John the Baptist preach. It was said he was announcing that their Deliverer was coming at last.

Late one evening, Jesus approached his mother. "Mother," he said respectfully, "I will soon be thirty years old. I must be about my Father's business."

Mary remembered the first time she heard Jesus say those words in the Temple—and the waves of panic and relief that had swept over her. Now those feelings came rushing back. But this day of separation was long coming, and she was ready to accept it, if only as a show of faith and love for God.

CHAPTER **1 4**

Jesus walked through the bushes toward the Jordan River near Bethabara, a small village south of the Sea of Galilee. The sound of water told him the river was close.

Then he heard a voice. As Jesus stepped out of the underbrush, the piercing bass voice of John the Baptist rang out, "REPENT! Prepare the way of the Lord."

Jesus smiled when he saw John the Baptist. Wild and uncivilized in his appearance, John stood in water up to his ankles as he spoke. Around him on the bank people sat on the rocks. All kinds of people had come to hear John—slaves, Roman soldiers, mothers with children.

Then Jesus noticed a cluster of men who were not enjoying the sermon. These were religious leaders, scribes and Pharisees. One of them interrupted John to ask: "Who are you?"

"I am the voice of one crying in the wilderness," John answered.

"Are you the Deliverer?" another demanded.

"No! I am here to prepare the way for Messiah." John had lived apart from the villages and their inhabitants for many years. He subsisted on a diet of locusts and honey and had little use for the religious establishment.

"Then why are you baptizing?" one of them asked him. John was usurping their authority. He baptized people rather than sending them to the Temple to offer sacrifices. Only Gentiles who wished to become Jews were required to undergo such ritual cleansing. By baptizing Jews, John made no distinction between Gentiles and God's chosen people.

One of the scribes spoke up angrily, saying, "Are we also to be baptized?"

"You brood of vipers!" John shouted, incensed. "The axe is already at the root of the trees, and every tree that does not produce good fruit will be cut down and thrown into the fire."

"What should we do then?" someone in the crowd called out.

"The man with two tunics should share with him who has none, and the one who has food should do the same."

A Roman soldier sitting with a few comrades stood up. "And what should we do?"

John replied, "Don't extort money and don't accuse the people falsely."

The people murmured, again wondering if John might be Christ, their Deliverer. John answered, saying, "I baptize you with water. But One more powerful than I will come, whose sandals I am not fit to carry. Even now he is among us."

Scandalized, the scribes and Pharisees refused to hear any more. They scooped up fistfuls of sand and threw it into the air, cursing John. Then they departed.

The following day, John again preached to the hundreds assembled at the river. When he gave his invitation to the people to be baptized, Jesus stepped into the river.

Jesus was unremarkable in appearance, his features plain. But when John saw Jesus coming to him, the Baptist stopped in midsentence. With the confidence of heaven and assurance in his heart, John pointed to Jesus: "Behold, the Lamb of God who takes away the sin of the world!"

A murmur started, low but grew steadily. "Does John know this man?" "What does the Baptist mean, 'Lamb of God'?" "Surely John doesn't believe this man is the Messiah!"

Jesus splashed through the shallow water to where John was standing. Each man looked into the other's soul. Finally, Jesus broke the silence. "I am ready to be baptized," he said, smiling.

"You are the One sent by God," John said. "I need to be baptized by *you*."

"Allow this," Jesus said, "because it is the right and proper thing to fulfill all that God requires."

So, John the Baptist placed his hands on the chest and back of Jesus and dipped him into the waters. When he raised him from the river, Jesus was smiling. The crowd on the riverbank did not understand what they had just seen.

Jesus stood praying there in the shallow waters when there came a sound like thunder. Then John saw him. Silently . . . harmlessly . . . just as a dove rests on the branch of a tree, the Holy Spirit descended from heaven and rested gently on Jesus.

Then came a voice from heaven. Everyone heard it, though many were unsure of what they heard. Still, those who truly believed, whose hearts swelled at this remarkable visitation, heard clearly the voice of the living God. "You are my beloved Son, in whom I am well pleased."

 CHAPTER **1 5**

The young fishermen had grown up together in Bethsaida. Andrew and John trusted each other. As followers of John the Baptist they had often talked late into the night about the promised Messiah. "Get ready for his coming," the Baptist preached.

Yesterday, Andrew and John had witnessed the baptism of a man named Jesus, whom John the Baptist had declared the "Lamb of God." Both friends had heard the voice of God.

When they saw Jesus walking among the crowds the next day, Andrew and John followed him, at first from a distance. After a few moments, Jesus stopped and confronted them. "What do you seek?"

Andrew, spoke up. "Rabbi . . . . he spoke the title "rabbi" with reverence, surprising John with his use of the honorific word for "teacher." "Rabbi, where are you living?"

"Come and see." Jesus said, "We'll eat together."

Soon it would be dark—Jesus, Andrew and John settled around a simple meal.

"If you are the Messiah," Andrew asked, "why did you not preach to the multitudes today?" Andrew believed the Jews would acknowledge their Deliverer and follow him. John pointed out that more than a thousand men had been present that day at the river; they could have formed the nucleus of a formidable army.

"My kingdom will not come by war," Jesus explained. "I must rule the hearts of people. I must rule within before I rule without."

Jesus taught them what the Messiah would do, tracing God's plan for the redemption of mankind. Beginning with the Torah—the first five books of Scripture—through the books of the prophets Jesus showed them what God had said about his Anointed One. And he had piercing questions for these young men.

"What does God want you to do with your life?"

Neither man was sure how to answer.

"When will you begin searching for God's will?"

"Now," they promised.

"Come, follow me." Jesus said. "Then you will go tell others about the kingdom."

The next morning the young men were gone. But Jesus knew they had not rejected what he taught them; these were true seekers whose hearts were open to the things of God.

Later, as Jesus was returning on the road to Galilee, Andrew came walking swiftly from the other direction. Someone was with him. Andrew waved, then yelled, "This is my brother. I told him you are the Messiah."

A tall man with a broad chest, Simon was ten years older than Andrew. "Are you the Christ?" he yelled as they approached.

Jesus laughed at the boldness of the man, then looked into his eyes. "You are Simon, son of Jonah," Jesus said to him, "but from now on you shall be called Peter. You will be like a rock."

"You are a blunt speaker," Jesus noted. "I will need you to help build my kingdom."

Turning to Andrew, Jesus said, "I will need your sensitivity and insight in the kingdom. You are careful of people's feelings."

They walked on. Soon they met young John and his brother James. Brawny and tall, James didn't say much, though like his brother he had a fiery temperament.

"I don't like to speak," James said to Jesus, "but if you are who they say, I'll do anything you ask."

 CHAPTER **1 6**

The following day, Jesus and his four new friends walked north into Galilee. By mid-afternoon they arrived at Tiberias, a fortified Roman city.

John had had a number of run-ins with Roman troops and he wanted nothing to do with the three soldiers now standing guard at the gate.

Jesus paid no attention to the soldiers. As he and his friends entered the city, a guard called out, "Hey! Where are you going?" Rumors of a Deliverer among the Jews had reached the ears of

Herod, and his centurions were ordered to suppress any attempts to form a rebel army.

Jesus smiled at the soldiers. "I am going to Cana where my cousin is to be married. These men are my disciples . . . I am a teacher."

"JOHN!" a voice rang out from inside the gate.

"PHILIP!" John immediately forgot about the soldiers and stepped through the gate to greet his childhood friend. Philip was short and skinny, an unlikely recruit for a military uprising. The Roman guard waved Jesus and his friends through the gate.

"Where have you been?" Philip interrogated John. John explained that he had been with John the Baptist at the Jordan River until he met Jesus. He told him of how Jesus had taught them from the Scriptures, revealing himself to be the one they had been waiting for.

Jesus stepped over to where the two friends were talking, and Philip looked at him.

Jesus said only, "Come. Follow me."

Philip left Tiberias to follow Jesus. Five friends who had grown up in Bethsaida were now reunited.

As they neared Cana, Philip left the group to walk ahead. Philip sought his friend Nathanael, who lived just outside Cana on a small farm. They were unlikely friends—Philip from poor parents who lived in an obscure fishing village; Nathanael had royal blood flowing in his veins.

Philip found Nathanael reading a scroll from the Scriptures, the words of the prophet Isaiah.

"We have found the Messiah," Philip said, "the one Isaiah and the prophets described."

"Who is this Messiah?" Nathanael asked.

"He is called Jesus of Nazareth, the son of Joseph."

A scowl darkened Nathanael's face. "Nazareth! Can anything good come out of there?" He had nothing against the sleepy village, but as a student of the Scriptures, he expected the Messiah to come out of Bethlehem.

"Come and see for yourself," Philip answered. The two left Nathanael's house and walked to where Jesus and his followers were staying.

When he saw Nathanael, Jesus announced, "Behold, an Israelite in whom there is no deceit! Nathanael, you are a sincere seeker. . . ."

"How do you know me?" Nathanael asked. "You haven't talked to me."

"I saw you under the fig tree where Philip found you praying," Jesus explained. "I have seen your heart and know you seek first the kingdom of God."

Nathanael looked to Philip. *Only God knows all things,* Nathanael thought. With his head bowed, he said, "Rabbi, you are the Son of God! You are the King of Israel."

Jesus lifted Nathanael's head. "Follow me, and you'll see far greater things."

CHAPTER **17**

"JESUS!"

The young Galilean men gathered around Jesus turned to see a middle-aged woman waving to them.

"Jesus," she repeated the name of her oldest son.

"Thank you for coming to your cousin's wedding," Mary said.

They were interrupted by a demanding voice from the house. "Mary, the wine is running low!" Levi, the master of ceremonies, was an elderly man, short and thin. His voice was quiet, but insistent.

"Jesus!" Levi raised his voice when he recognized his nephew. Jesus introduced his disciples to his uncle, who in turn responded, "You must come and eat with us."

After meeting the guests and the families of the wedded couple, the young men took their places at the table.

"Bring them a plate of food," Mary instructed the servants. Quickly, warm bread appeared, and lamb stew.

At the head of the table, Levi told stories. There was laughter and there were more than a few red faces.

While Levi was speaking, Mary whispered to Jesus, "There's no more wine. The pitchers are empty. What am I to do?"

"Why do you come to me? You are responsible for the food at this wedding," Jesus said to her.

"But I am not the one who will bear the shame," Mary thought aloud. "Levi and this poor young couple will suffer the humiliation of failing to provide for their guests."

Jesus left the festivities and walked outside to the back of the house. The servants followed, watching him.

Against a corner of the house were six water pots, each of a different size and color. Jesus turned to the servants and said, "Fill each one to the top with water. Then take the pots to Levi."

The servants quickly took small vessels and filled the larger pots. Then, picking up the pots, they started toward the door. "Attention, everyone!" Levi managed to conceal his relief at the arrival of additional wine. "Let's have a toast to the bride and groom."

The table grew silent. Panic flashed in the servants' faces. They placed a large pot on the floor on either side of Levi. Levi took his cup and dipped into the water pot. Since it was customary for the master to drink first, he put the cup to his lips.

"Ah-h-h," he sighed. Then Levi's crinkled eyes and deep smile suddenly vanished. He stared unbelievingly into his cup. "Why have you hidden the best wine until now? Every man sets out the good wine first. But *you* have saved the best for last!"

Levi laughed. The groom laughed. The guests all laughed. But the servants began jabbering among themselves. John turned to his brother James and whispered, "The servants claim Jesus turned water into wine."

The disciples talked excitedly between themselves. Was this possible?

"Tell us what you are saying!" Levi called to James and John. John spoke carefully. "The vintage you are drinking came from the pots that catch rain. An hour ago, it was not wine, but water."

Levi commanded that the servants be brought to him. "Where did you get this wine?" he demanded.

The head servant spoke with his eyes downcast. "Your nephew, the son of Mary, commanded us to fill the pots to the brim with water. We do not know how he did it, but the water became wine!"

The room fell silent. All eyes turned to Jesus, but Jesus was not there. He had departed before the wine was served.

 CHAPTER **1 8**

Dark clouds scurried across the sky above the mountains. Jesus was tiring. He had traversed one hill after another toward his destination: an uninhabited peak barren of life.

The Spirit of God had led Jesus to this desolate place, but he was not alone; an evil presence shadowed the man from Nazareth.

Jesus crossed the Wadi Qelt and began to climb the rocks, then stumbled into a pass flanked by formidable cliffs. Nearby, a spring of water trickled through the rocks and Jesus drank from it. He followed the spring to a cave that would protect him from the elements.

A red serpent hissed and slithered out from under a rock. Across the ravine, two wolves stood in a cave. Jesus ignored them. Soon a far more dangerous predator would stalk him.

Jesus lay exhausted on the cave floor, but could not sleep. He had committed himself not to eat any food for forty days.

But there was an emptiness inside that bread and wine could not fill; for Jesus was hungry for God.

The days passed. A storm rumbled through the valley, the clouds unleashing their frigid contents. Jesus pulled his cloak tightly about him.

As Jesus approached the end of his fast, he found he was lonely. He had not heard another human voice for forty days. A snowflake softly lit on the back of his folded hands. Then another. Jesus prayed before dozing with white drifting in the ravine.

The next morning Jesus awakened to a sound, like the squeak of a chariot wheel. Then he recognized the chirping of a bird.

Morning washed away the night, and the sun peered down into the ravine. "The sun," Jesus said aloud. "God is good." He was ready to do battle.

His adversary, Satan, had been waiting and watching. Now he came to Jesus in the small clearing. "If you are the Son of God," he challenged Jesus, "command these stones to become loaves of bread. You must be hungry."

The aroma of fresh bread drifted through Jesus' memory. But the Father had sent him to serve mankind, not himself.

"No," Jesus said. "For it is written, 'Man shall not live by bread alone, but by every word that proceeds from the mouth of God.'"

Satan, still confident, changed tactics. The two enemies were transported to the pinnacle of the Temple in Jerusalem, where they could look down on Jerusalem—and Jerusalem could see them. Satan challenged Jesus: "The people want miracles. Throw yourself off the pinnacle. The angels will save you . . . people will believe in you."

Jesus would indeed do miracles, but he would not do one for Satan. He would do only the will of his Father. Jesus answered the devil, saying, "It is also written: 'Do not tempt the Lord your God.'"

Then they were whisked to the peak of a mountain. From there, they looked out on the majesty of all the kingdoms of the world. In one transcending moment, Jesus saw the nations of the earth. *They are the reason why I have come*, he thought.

"I am the god of this world," Satan boasted, "and these are my people." Jesus did not deny this. Satan reigned on earth and enslaved its people. Jesus' heart ached for them.

"If you bow down to me . . . ," the devil propositioned, "I will give all these people to you."

No mortal man will ever know how deeply Jesus was tempted to strike this bargain, because mortal men will never love the people of the world as Jesus loved them at that moment.

"Away with you, Satan!" Jesus answered. "For it is written, 'You shall worship the Lord your God, and you shall serve him only.'"

 CHAPTER **19**

A severe spring storm had rumbled across the Sea of Galilee the previous evening, and the fishermen who braved the storm were unable to catch anything. But morning broke with an unusual calm. Peter looked in the water and saw a perfect reflection of his red beard and red eyes.

"We'll have to work all morning." Peter began pulling on the rain-soaked nets. "We have to make up for lost time." Andrew didn't answer but jumped up to help him.

"Let's cast near the shore," Peter said to his brother. "The fish may be hiding among the shoals." Andrew piloted the boat toward shore, near where James and John sat with their father Zebedee, mending nets.

Peter clambered out of the boat and waded knee deep into the lake. Andrew began tossing the wet nets from the boat.

"Any more news of Jesus?" Peter asked his brother. They hadn't seen Jesus for weeks.

The brothers discussed their doubts. Jesus was not at all what they expected of a Messiah. They had been looking for a warrior who would lead Israel into battle.

Young John asked, "James, do you believe Jesus is the Messiah?"

James weighed his answer carefully. Finally, he nodded his head, answering simply, "Yes."

While the fishermen worked and discussed the Messiah, they didn't see Jesus coming along the beach. A large crowd was following him. It was the crowd the fishermen saw first, and John recognized Philip and Nathanael among them. Then the fisherman saw Jesus.

Jesus stepped out onto a few large rocks in the water. "Come!" He beckoned. "Follow me, and I will make you fishers of men."

Peter knew in his heart that Jesus was much more than a teacher. He immediately dropped his nets and sloshed through the water toward Jesus. Andrew folded his nets, then followed his brother.

CHAPTER **20**

The synagogue in Capernaum lay nestled among tall sycamores. It was a quiet Sabbath day much like any other, but excitement swept a small horde of villagers toward the synagogue. Jesus and his disciples walked at the front, laughing and talking.

As the people entered the building, each man draped a prayer shawl over his head. Everyone joined in singing psalms.

Five elders stood to read from the Law. An elder then nodded his head to Jesus to read from the *Haphtarah*. Unrolling the scroll, Jesus read declaratively from the text. He followed the Jewish custom of *charaz*, teaching the people verse to verse, passage to passage, like pearls on a necklace.

As Jesus approached the end of his lesson, he called for commitment to the heavenly Father. Suddenly a demonic voice shrieked from the rear of the synagogue. The elders craned their heads in disbelief.

"Eeeeeeeeeekkkk!" came the shriek again.

"Quiet." The calm but penetrating voice of Jesus hushed the crowd. Jesus walked to where a man stood shaking.

Demon possession was not new to the worshipers. Somewhere between the conscious and unconscious, a vulgar personality had invaded this man, and taken possession of his personality.

Snorting and shaking, the man vomited, then yelled out, "You have no control over me, Jesus of Nazareth!"

Jesus was not intimidated, nor did he attempt to restrain the man.

Again, the voice of the demon challenged Jesus: "I know who you are. I know you are the Holy One of God."

The demon spoke in Hebrew, calling Jesus by the name Satan coveted, the title used to describe God. Jesus, however, would not allow a demon to proclaim him Messiah.

"Be quiet!" Jesus commanded, and the voice was gagged. Jesus commanded the demon to relinquish the man's body: "Come out of him!"

The man slumped in his seat, falling against the rear wall. Jesus returned to the lectern and rolled the scroll back into place. He gave it to the scribe to be replaced in its container. Then he motioned to his disciples, and left the synagogue.

The home of Simon Peter and Andrew was located on the main thoroughfare that stretched from the front steps of the synagogue to the public dock. Jesus indicated to the disciples that they would stop there.

CHAPTER **21**

As those inside the home of Simon Peter and Andrew enjoyed the Sabbath meal, a crowd was gathering in the street. The lame, the injured, the sick and the demon-possessed of Capernaum lay on pallets, while the whole city gathered and waited.

After the Sabbath service, word had spread that Jesus had cast an evil spirit out of a man in the synagogue. Many had heard the demon cry out before fleeing. After the services, they had run to their friends and neighbors to tell what they saw. "Come with us," they encouraged all who were sick. "Come with us, and we will take you to Jesus."

The door finally opened, and all eyes were on Jesus as he stepped into the street, followed by John and James.

No one called out, and Jesus said nothing, but began going from pallet to pallet touching the sick and healing them. His voice was quiet and compassionate, and no one dared speak. One by one the people thanked him, and he moved on.

John observed the scene but remained detached. Rather than recruiting soldiers, the Messiah attracted the sick and helpless—people who couldn't take up arms against the Romans. And yet Jesus inspired fierce devotion. Perhaps, if the people were organized properly . . . .

Jesus and his disciples left the home of Peter and Andrew after breakfast, and by noon they were winding their way up the mountain to a village that could be seen from Capernaum. John walked apart from the others, deep in thought.

The main group followed the path along the wall of the small city, then, abruptly turning left through a gate, went out of John's view. Before John could catch up, he heard noises from the other side of the wall. At first he feared for Jesus' safety. Then he heard a shout: "Keep away! Unclean!"

Young John rushed to where Jesus and the other disciples had stopped just inside the village gate. From the village came limping a man, a leper, pursued by a small group of men and women throwing stones at him. The lower part of his face was eaten away by scabs, and his upper lip was covered with sores. When the leper saw Jesus, he cried with a loud voice what he was required by law: "Unclean . . . Unclean. . . ."

As a young boy, John had been taught that leprosy was a result of sin.

This leper, wrapped in funeral clothes, retreated against the city wall to let Jesus and the disciples pass. When the leper stopped at the wall, the villagers backed off. Jews were not to come within six feet of a leper.

Much to the surprise of the disciples and the villagers, the leper began approaching Jesus. He fell with his face to the ground and cried out, "If you are willing, you can make me clean."

John wondered, *How does a leper know of Jesus?*

Jesus looked down at the man with tenderness. Then to John's horror, Jesus knelt and reached his hand toward the leper. Leprosy was highly contagious.

"I am willing," Jesus placed his hand on the head of the leper. "Be clean!"

Jesus removed his hand, and after a moment the man stirred. He slowly looked up at Jesus, and John caught sight of the man's face. The sores, the scabs, the rotted flesh—all were gone. His face was instead wet; he was crying.

Jesus commanded the man to stand up. "Now you must go."

"But. . . ," the man began.

"See that you tell no one. Let the priest tell the people that you are healed."

The disciples knew the words of Moses well. This man's only way back into public acceptance was through the public pronouncement of the priest.

John wondered if the wiser course would be to have the leper stay with them, for he bore a tremendous witness to the power of Jesus. Yet, Jesus did not want crowds following him. He had come to teach and preach the kingdom of heaven: already, on several occasions, Jesus had pointed his disciples away from the miracles to his greater mission.

CHAPTER **22**

When it was nearly time for the Jewish Passover, Jesus and his disciples made the journey to Jerusalem. As when he was a child, Jesus was immediately drawn to the Temple. But something was different now. A throng of beggars blocked their way, shouting and pleading. Trash was everywhere.

Peter saw it first. A scowl had come over the face of Jesus. His usually calm demeanor had dissolved into irritation.

Inside the Temple, loud voices filled the courtyard. The Galileans had expected to hear Levites singing psalms. But instead of reverence, they saw a tumultuous crowd. People were buying and selling in the outer courtyard. Moneychangers were negotiating with worshipers to change foreign coins into Hebrew currency for temple offerings.

Then there was the selling of livestock and birds for sacrifices. One farmer held several oxen by a harness. Another had a small pen for lambs. Still another had a gigantic bull he was trying to sell. "If you have a big sin, I have a big bull," he hollered.

Jesus and his followers stood and surveyed the mob. Jesus looked about for a priest, but the priests were nowhere to be seen.

His nostrils flaring, Jesus picked up three leather cords laying near him on the ground. He walked up the stairs and out onto a small wall where he could be seen. Then, lifting his voice, he cried, "How dare you turn my Father's house into a market! This is not a house of merchandise!"

Laughter erupted from the businessmen.

"Stop!" Jesus yelled out over the crowd. Silence began to ripple out to the edges of the courtyard.

"This is a house of prayer," Jesus' voice echoed. "Take your business outside the Temple. Now!"

There was absolute silence. No one moved.

The owner of the bull pointed at Jesus and shouted, "Why don't you take your business outside." He laughed at Jesus. The crowd that had been given over to unrestrained haggling now united in scorn.

Leaping down and stepping over to a table, Jesus kicked it over with a thunderous crash. He unleashed his wrath on the moneychangers' tables, overturning each of them in succession. Coins flew every which way. Cages crashed to the ground as Jesus stormed through the courtyard, turtledoves and pigeons fluttering free.

With his makeshift whip in hand and his face flushed with anger, Jesus stepped toward the man with the bull. The man stumbled backwards and the bull bolted toward the exit. Merchants and customers scattered like leaves.

The businessmen had escaped, but many honest worshipers were still there. They were stunned yet scared, not knowing what Jesus would do to them.

"My Father's house is to be a house of prayer," Jesus announced to them.

Slowly, priests began appearing in the courtyard. One by one they appeared. They surveyed the coins on the floor, the broken pens and the overturned tables.

One of the priests walked over to Jesus. "By what authority do you clear the Temple?" he asked.

Jesus didn't answer.

"The priests are the keepers of the Temple," the priest said. The other priests nodded.

Jesus ignored him.

"Are you not Jesus of Nazareth?" he asked. Word had reached Jerusalem of a Galilean doing miracles with wine. "What miraculous sign can you show us to prove your authority to do this?" the priest asked.

"If you destroy this Temple," Jesus now said in answer, "I will raise it again in three days."

"It has taken forty-six years to build this Temple," the priest mockingly answered, "and you think you can rebuild it in three days?"

No one fully understood what Jesus meant. But Jesus spoke of his own death and resurrection, which he knew was coming. Jesus remained in Jerusalem for Passover. He continued teaching and performing miracles. The Temple merchants stayed out of his way and for the rest of the week they kept their merchandise out of the Temple.

The priests continued to discuss Jesus among themselves. He had challenged their authority.

CHAPTER **23**

Word had spread quickly through the small village. The son of Mary and Joseph had returned to Nazareth and had been asked to speak at the synagogue, though his mother and brothers had since moved to Capernaum.

Jesus entered the synagogue and took a seat reserved for visiting speakers. When the time came for him to speak, the leader of the synagogue selected the writings of Isaiah, and handed the scroll to Jesus. Jesus carefully unrolled the scroll to where Isaiah prophesied concerning the Messiah, then read aloud:

"The Spirit of the Lord is upon Me, because He has anointed Me to preach the gospel to the poor; He has sent Me to heal the broken-hearted, to proclaim liberty to the captives and recovery of sight to the blind, to set at liberty those who are oppressed; to proclaim the acceptable year of the Lord."

Jesus rolled the scroll back into place and returned it to the leader. Then he sat down. Every eye in the room looked at him. They were waiting for his sermon.

But all Jesus said was, "Today this Scripture is fulfilled in your hearing."

The elders began to shake their heads in disapproval. The passage he had read referred to the coming Messiah. The word that jumped to their minds was *blasphemy*, but no one wanted to say that word. This was Joseph's son.

"No!" one of the elders dared to say out loud. "You may be a worker of miracles, but you cannot call yourself Messiah!"

Jesus knew they came to see miracles but did not believe in him. He said, "Many of you want me to do miracles in Nazareth as I have done at Capernaum and at Jerusalem. But I say to you, no prophet is accepted in his hometown."

The minister of the synagogue asked, "Why will you not show us what you can do? If you are the Messiah, give us a sign."

Jesus didn't answer him directly, but spoke to the congregation: "In the time of Elisha, there were many lepers in Israel, but none of them were cleansed except Naaman, a Syrian. I cannot do miracles in my hometown because of your unbelief. You will not believe that I am who I say I am."

The synagogue erupted in indignation. Jesus had told them they were not fit for miracles.

Voices began to swell like thunder, and the Nazarenes drove Jesus out of their synagogue. They cursed him and forced him to the outskirts of town.

Just outside Nazareth, the road to Capernaum passed dangerously close to a forty-foot cliff. They pushed Jesus up the hill toward the cliff, determined to throw him off. Jesus allowed himself to be pressed forward until they reached the brow of the hill.

Then he turned and looked upon his pursuers, and the mob was silenced. They held their collective breath, waiting for Jesus to speak. But Jesus said nothing. He walked back down the hill, and went his way.

CHAPTER **2 4**

The road from Damascus to Egypt ran alongside the outer wall of Capernaum; the calls of camel drivers to their animals drifted over the wall. Jesus and his disciples exited Capernaum through the city gate, turned left on the Roman road and began walking south in the direction of Judea.

Almost immediately, they encountered the customs booth where taxes were collected. Philip counted the number of camels in front of him, then remarked to Nathanael, "It will take a long while to get through the tax line today."

Philip was annoyed, but it couldn't be helped. Capernaum was the convergence of most traveled roads in Galilee, so that's where taxes were collected.

Everything that went through customs was taxed—grain, wine, cloth, produce of all kinds. To add to the burden, Levi, the chief tax collector for Herod in Capernaum, collected *ad valorem* on everything that passed his table: axles, wheels, pack animals and anything else he could think of to tax. Thus he had become extremely wealthy.

Because they ruled over everything that passed through their domains, tax collectors were thought to be oppressors. Rabbis expelled at once any Jew who accepted a job collecting taxes for the Romans.

Levi was philosophical about his ejection from the synagogue in Capernaum. But deep down he knew he was a sinful man. Levi had seen the crowds listening intently to this new teacher.

When he looked up to see Jesus in the tax line, Levi wanted to say something to him, but he didn't know how to greet him. As Jesus stepped to Levi's table, Jesus said to him simply, "Follow me."

With this simple invitation of Jesus, Levi saw his past swallowed up. And an overwhelming sense of relief washed over him.

Levi left the booth to follow Jesus.

Jesus looked behind him and smiled. He said, "You will be called Matthew, for you are a gift of God."

 CHAPTER **25**

When Jesus returned to Jerusalem to observe the Feast of Passover, he had gained popularity with the people. His reputation with the religious authorities had worsened, however.

As Jesus and his disciples walked to the Temple to worship on the Sabbath day, Andrew drew their attention down the street to where a throng had gathered at the pool of Bethesda. It was said that an angel stirred up the pool from time to time, and the first person to enter the pool after the water erupted would be healed.

"There must be more than two thousand people at the pool," Andrew cautioned Jesus. "If we go down this side street, we can bypass the crowd."

Jesus shook his head and continued walking. As they approached the pool, they heard an argument. At the edge of the pool, people were elbowing for position near the waters.

"I was here first," a voice rang out.

"I was here yesterday," another protested.

Slowly Jesus eased through the crowd, looking from one face to the next. Then, seeing a man against a wall, Jesus began walking toward him.

The poor man's worn pallet showed the wear and tear of being rolled and unrolled every day for thirty-eight years. Each day during that time, the lame man had waited in vain for the moving of the waters, knowing full well that when the waters were stirred he could not be first in.

The man slumped against the wall, his hope long depleted. In an act of rebellion against God nearly four decades earlier, something happened to cripple him. Because of one act of rebellion, he had never walked again.

"Do you want to be healed?" Jesus asked.

"Sir, I don't have anyone to help me into the pool."

Jesus commanded the lame man, "Rise! Pick up your mat and walk."

Instantly, the man felt sensations he hadn't felt for thirty-eight years. He stood! No one around him noticed, and he did not yell, scream or dance. He had been told to take up his mat and walk, so he obeyed.

Jesus continued walking through the crowd. Because all eyes were fixed on the water, none had seen the miracle.

But a pair of Jewish leaders walking to the Temple immediately spotted the healed man. "THIS IS THE SABBATH DAY!" they shouted. "PUT THAT MAT DOWN!"

The Sabbath day had been instituted as a sign of God's covenant with his people. Just as God rested from his work on the seventh day, so the Jews were to work six days and rest on the seventh. But through the years Jewish leaders had developed so many regulations, the meaning of the Sabbath had become hopelessly obscured.

Under the rabbinical interpretations of the Law, carrying a pallet was considered "work" and was therefore illegal. So the Pharisees accosted the once-lame man.

"It is not lawful for you to carry your bed on the Sabbath day. Why do you do this?"

"The man who made me well said, 'Pick up your mat and walk.'"

"What was the man's name?" the Jewish leaders insisted. "I don't know. I didn't ask his name."

To get away from the Pharisees, the man was forced to throw his pallet to the ground. Just as quickly, a thief came along and took it.

The healed man walked straight to the gate of the Temple. He knew well the commandment in Scripture, that those with physical ailments could not enter the House of God. For thirty-eight years as a lame man, he had not been inside the Temple. But now he walked into God's house.

Now inside the Temple, he wanted to say to God, "Thank you for healing me."

Suddenly, Jesus was there. "God has heard your prayers," he said.

The healed man's eyes welled up with tears of gratitude.

But Jesus did not seek the man's gratitude, he sought his heart. He searched the man's eyes. "Do not go back to the sin that crippled you."

Then Jesus turned and melted into the crowd.

Unknown to the man, the Pharisees had been watching. They had recognized Jesus, and approached the man.

"Was that the man who healed you?" they demanded. The healed man nodded.

"Did he tell you to pick up your bed and walk?"

"Yes."

Immediately the priests stormed through the crowds after Jesus. Not only had he healed the lame man—surely this must be defined as "work"—but he had incited the man to break the Sabbath! They finally caught up to him near the Gate Beautiful.

"Why do you violate the Sabbath?"

Jesus smiled a knowing smile and nodded his head. He said to them, "My Father is always ready to work on the Sabbath day, and so the Son must work while he is on earth."

"Blasphemy!" a priest shouted. Jesus had proclaimed himself the Son of God.

By now a large crowd was gathering, drawn by the shouting. If they had been outside the Temple, the crowd would have stoned him. Jesus saw the rage in their hearts, but continued speaking.

"I tell you the truth, the Son can do nothing by himself. He can do only what he sees his Father doing. For the Father loves the Son and shows him all things. You have never heard his voice nor seen his form, nor does his word dwell in you, for you do not believe the one he sent."

The priests retired to discuss what they had just heard, and plotted how they could put Jesus to death.

CHAPTER **2 6**

Knowing the religious authorities plotted against his life, Jesus withdrew with his disciples to the Sea of Galilee. A great multitude followed.

The crowds pressed in on Jesus so much he was unable to talk with his disciples. He asked that a small boat be kept ready to take him across the sea should the crowd grow unruly.

He needed help to minister to the multitudes. Jesus needed a small number of close associates whom he could direct and guide. This smaller circle of men would learn from his example, then they would teach others.

Jesus climbed into the boat and sailed away, leaving the crowd on shore. Arriving near Magdala, he left the craft on the beach and climbed a steep hill, looking for a place where he could be alone. Tonight, Jesus would come to the most important decision in his ministry.

All those who faithfully followed him were known as his "disciples," but Jesus would call his chosen twelve "apostles," a Greek word that meant sent ones. The twelve apostles would be the ones he would send to carry the gospel, or good news, to the entire earth.

Falling to his knees, Jesus began praying. "Lord . . . help me choose those that can be trusted with your words."

Jesus prayed all night. When the sun peeked over the eastern mountains, he came down from the hill to where the disciples were waiting.

Jesus said to them. "All of you will continue to follow me. You will all be called disciples. But only twelve will be apostles. They will preach and be given power to heal sickness and cast out demons."

Jesus looked from face to face. "Simon will be first," Jesus nodded to the strapping fisherman. "Simon will be called Peter, for he will be strong."

His next choice was James. Everyone was surprised by this choice, because James was so quick to anger. The third choice was his brother John, the youngest of all the disciples.

Jesus said, "James and John are as thunder; they will roar like the thunderstorm at sin or iniquity."

Jesus selected Andrew as his fourth apostle. Once a follower of John the Baptist, Andrew was sensitive to the needs of people. "Philip, you too will be an apostle. Philip will be in charge of the next three apostles and will supervise the crowds, arrange accommodations and other details."

Jesus appointed three other apostles to serve with Philip: his friend Nathanael; Matthew, the former tax collector; and Thomas, who was known for his pragmatism.

"The ninth apostle will be James, son of Alphaeus," Jesus nodded to the shortest of his disciples. "Your group will be in charge of our money."

To work with James, Jesus called Thaddeus and Simon the Zealot.

The first eleven men that Jesus chose were from Galilee. They spoke with a Galilean accent, and understood the area from which Jesus came.

Then Jesus announced, "Judas Iscariot will be my twelfth apostle. He is the one especially chosen by my Father." He assigned Judas to carry the money bag.

CHAPTER **27**

The morning broke soft over the hills around Tiberias. Jesus left the highway and began to climb. He pointed to the top of a small hill.

"Up there," he said.

At the pinnacle of the hill, the mount flattened out and Jesus sat on a rock with his disciples.

But they were not alone. The multitudes had followed Jesus. Every day, more and more people were coming to be near him. "Blessed are you who depend only on the Father, for yours is the kingdom," Jesus said to them.

"Blessed are you who mourn, for you shall be comforted.

"Blessed are you who are humble, for you shall inherit the earth.

"Blessed are you who thirst after righteousness, for you shall be filled.

"Blessed are you who show mercy to others, for you shall obtain mercy.

"Blessed are you who have a pure heart, for you shall see God.

"Blessed are you who make peace between warring factions, for you shall be called the children of God.

"Blessed are you who are persecuted for doing what is right, for yours is the kingdom of heaven.

"Blessed are you when men hate you, persecute you and lie about you because of me. Rejoice and be glad, because great is your reward in heaven."

Jesus taught them that the kingdom of God was not a place that could be seen or visited, but that the kingdom lived within those who believed. And, rules meant nothing if one's heart was not right.

"The Law says, 'Do not murder.' But I tell you do not get angry with your brother or even think about killing. The Law says,

'Do not commit adultery.' But I say to you do not even think lustful thoughts."

"Love your enemies. Bless those who curse you, do good to those who hate you and pray for those who spitefully use you."

"Do not worry about your life, what you are going to eat, what you are going to drink. Do not worry about your body or what you will wear. Seek first the kingdom of God, and all these things will be given to you."

"None of you can add one inch to your stature by worrying. Look at the lilies of the field and see how they grow. They do not labor, neither do they spin. Yet I tell you that not even Solomon in all his splendor was dressed like one of these flowers. If that is how God clothes the grass of the field, how much more is he able to take care of you?"

Jesus said, "Ask and it will be given to you. Seek and you will find. Knock and the door will be opened to you."

The apostles marveled at this teaching. Jesus was throwing open the gates to his kingdom, and anyone who would come to Jesus and follow him could enter.

And the people were astonished, because this is not what they had been taught in the synagogues. Yet Jesus taught with authority far greater than that of the keepers of the Law. So people listened and believed because he loved them.

CHAPTER **28**

Magdala was a short journey from Tiberias. Celebrated for its dye-works, the city's main commerce was the manufacture of textiles.

The last time Jesus had journeyed through Magdala, a woman in black had come running down the road, hissing and spitting at him. Jesus was moved with compassion for her. He cast out seven evil spirits from within her and healed her infirmities. In gratitude, this woman, Mary, had gone from home to home in Magdala telling everyone about Jesus.

Now when Jesus returned, Mary met him in the road.

"We must follow you," she said, pointing to a group of women. "We want to help in any way possible."

Jesus laughed joyfully and gave his permission.

As Jesus traveled from one village to another, the twelve apostles stayed close by him, while Mary Magdalene and the other women fell in behind them. But among the multitudes was a group of Pharisees, scribes and other critics of Jesus, watching and waiting to make accusations against him.

CHAPTER **2 9**

John the Baptist had been imprisoned for publicly denouncing the relationship between Herod Antipas and his brother's wife, Herodias. Herodias had been married to her older half-uncle Philip, the son of Herod the Great. Although Philip had an immense fortune, he had no political power. His young wife wanted more. So Herodias seduced Philip's half-brother Herod Antipas, the tetrarch of Galilee. Herodias had his own wife executed, then took Herodias to be his wife, even while Philip lived.

No one in the religious community dared to speak out against their adulterous union except John the Baptist. Herod Antipas was inclined to overlook this outrage, because he liked the Baptist. But his new wife was vengeful. She vowed to rid herself of the preacher, and within a year she convinced Antipas to imprison him. The Baptist was arrested and placed in Machaerus, a fortress high up in the mountains on the eastern shore of the Dead Sea.

On an early spring evening, one week before Passover, the palace at Machaerus was lit up like a torch. The people in the town below could smell the tempting aromas and hear drunken laughter from the festive banquet. One course of food followed another. Wine and alcohol were abundant. Finally, Herod Antipas called for his guests to be entertained.

To the surprise of everyone, Salome, the daughter of Herodias, danced into the light. Salome danced magnificently, tempting and taunting the men. Herodias recognized the charms of her young daughter, and had coaxed her into this fleshly amusement to achieve her own ends. When Salome reached the end of her spectacle, the audience erupted in applause. Antipas jumped to his feet. With his guests as witnesses, he made a drunken vow to Salome: "You shall have anything you want, even half of my kingdom."

Salome smiled, her mother's words leaping out of her mouth: "Give me the head of John the Baptist on a silver platter."

Herod's countenance dropped. Anger gripped his heart, but he could not rescind his offer to Salome. He ordered his guards, "Go and bring me the head of the Baptist."

The executioner stepped out of the banquet hall into the cold night, walking up the steps from the palace to the prison. When he opened the rusty doors, John the Baptist knew that his end was at hand.

Within a few minutes, the guard was dashing down the stairs to the banquet hall, the head of John the Baptist held high for all to see. The piercing eyes of the dead Baptist were open. As the platter was offered up to Herod Antipas, John preached his final message: "REPENT."

CHAPTER **30**

Jesus was angered and heartbroken over the death of the prophet. The apostles encouraged him to speak against this atrocity. The youngest apostle John agreed with Simon that this might be the catalyst that would stir the Jews to war. But Jesus did not want a confrontation with Herod Antipas. This was not the battle he came to fight.

The roads were filled with pilgrims on their way to Jerusalem for Passover. Wanting to avoid the crowds and any speculation about what he would do, Jesus got into a boat with his apostles and headed north.

When men and women on the highway along the lake saw Jesus leave, many abandoned their pilgrimage and began following him along the shore. Jesus' boat landed near a large expanse of grass. He went to the top of a small hill to pray. But soon the multitudes gathered at the hill. When Jesus saw the people, as always his heart was moved. He began teaching them.

Because only men were required to attend Passover, many of their wives and children had stayed home. Jesus looked out to see thousands of strong men. If ever a dictator wanted an army to recruit and train for his purposes, this was the occasion. Jesus had only to proclaim himself their leader.

Jesus ministered all day. The apostle Philip was the first to notice the shadows falling over the crowd.

Philip spoke to Jesus. "Lord, this is a deserted place, and the hour is late. Send the multitudes away, so they may buy food."

Since Philip was in charge of food and provisions, Jesus asked him, "Where can we buy bread so that these people may eat?" Jesus was testing Philip; he already knew what he would do.

Philip had already counted the crowd. He knew there were about five thousand men there, plus a few hundred women and children. Philip answered, "Why, eight months of wages wouldn't feed this many!"

Philip sent the apostles into the crowd to inventory what food was available. Only Andrew found food. Andrew said to Jesus, "There is a little boy here. He has five barley loaves and two small fish, but what are they among so many?"

Jesus said to Philip, "Make the people sit down, and bring the loaves and fish to me."

The apostles followed Jesus' directions.

Jesus took the loaves, held them to heaven and gave thanks: "Blessed are you, our God, who calls this bread to come forth from the earth."

He directed the twelve to gather some baskets, then began breaking the loaves of bread, placing the morsels in a basket. He repeated the practice until the baskets were filled.

"Give this food to the people to eat," he said to Philip, who had watched the process. Then the apostles fanned out into the crowd. The baskets were never emptied, yet each person ate as much as he needed.

As the sun set, Jesus said to his apostles, "Gather up the fragments."

When the apostles had gathered up the fragments, there were twelve baskets left, one for each apostle—enough food for three or four days.

CHAPTER **31**

By the estimation of anyone in Palestine—Roman or Jew—five thousand well-fed men was a potential army. Here were five thousand men who wouldn't be distracted by hunger—Jesus could feed them miraculously. If they were wounded in battle, Jesus could heal them. Surely these men could be motivated to follow the Messiah in a campaign to liberate the Holy Land.

The same thoughts occurred to a number of the five thousand. The men were carried way with their potential and talked about making Jesus their king—by force if necessary.

Jesus directed the apostles toward the boat, then pointing across the sea, he instructed them, "Go to Capernaum."

Jesus walked swiftly through several clusters of excited men, then slipped between some high rocks into the hills. He needed to be alone, to pray and commune with the Father.

A desert storm rolled into the Sea of Galilee, and the hot air mixing with cool breezes off the cold water unleashed a torrential rain.

As Jesus was praying, he looked out and saw the disciples caught in the storm. If they tried to make it to shore, the boat would be pounded to pieces. If they stayed on the lake, the boat would capsize. Immediately, Jesus left his place of prayer and went to them, walking across the water.

The waves grew higher; even the apostles who were hardened fishermen were frightened.

"YE-E-E-A-A-A-I-I-I!" one of the apostles screamed. "It's a ghost!"

The scream startled the other apostles, who caught sight of the apparition walking on the water. They stopped pulling on the oars and stared, dumbstruck.

One of them yelled again, "It's a ghost!"

Peter didn't believe it. He knew this was no spirit, but someone dear. The stout, red-bearded fisherman yelled, "It's the Lord!"

Jesus called out, "It is I! Do not be afraid."

Ever impetuous, Peter shouted out over the water, "Lord . . . if it is you, tell me to come to you, and I will walk to you on the water."

This was the kind of faith Jesus had been waiting to see in his disciples. He said to Peter, "Come . . . ."

Instinctively, Peter leaped from the boat. He began walking toward his master on the water.

At first, the eyes of Peter were riveted to Jesus. In faith, the big fisherman was doing something no man had ever done. But when Peter saw the waves swirling around him, he became afraid and began to sink. Peter looked to Jesus with beseeching eyes. He cried out, "Lord, save me!"

Jesus stretched out a hand and caught him, asking, "O you of little faith, why did you doubt?"

When Jesus and Peter got into the boat, Jesus commanded the raging waves, "Peace . . . be still." And the wind ceased.

CHAPTER **32**

Rising dramatically more than nine thousand feet from the Syrian desert, Mount Hermon dominated the northern landscape of Galilee. Here, near the village of Caesarea Philippi, Jesus found rest out of reach of the massive crowds.

His ministry on earth was nearing its end. Soon the authorities would arrest him and charge him with crimes against the people and against God.

After a few days of rest, Jesus was ready to prepare the apostles for the coming time.

"There is something you need to know," Jesus said soberly. "Soon we are going up to Jerusalem. There, I must suffer at the hands of the priests and teachers of the law. They will kill me, but after three days, I will rise again."

"Never, Lord!" Peter pounded his fist. "We will never let them kill you!"

Jesus wheeled about at Peter's arrogance. "Get behind me, Satan! You are in my way."

Peter was stunned. He dropped to the ground, pulling his tunic around him in shame.

"If any man will come after me," Jesus said to them, "you must put aside any selfish ambition. For what profit is it to a man if he gains the whole world, and loses his own soul?"

None of the apostles slept soundly that evening. Jesus' message weighed heavily on their minds.

Six days later Jesus spoke privately to the three men closest to him. "Peter, James and John," he said, "come with me." He pointed to the peak of Mount Hermon.

They climbed all that day toward the snowcapped summit; Jesus climbing ahead of the others.

As John and his fellow apostles crested a plateau in the side of the mountain, the breeze picked up speed, blowing a cloud rapidly toward the plateau, where Jesus now stood about fifty paces away. John saw there was something unusual about this cloud. Rather than absorbing light, sunbeams danced off it.

The cloud settled over the plateau, covering them as a warm blanket. Peter, James and John looked for their master through the mist and then saw Jesus as they had never seen him.

He appeared opalescent, as though reflecting the light from the cloud.

Through the mist, two men appeared to talk with him. He conversed amiably with the men as though they were long lost friends.

"That's . . . that's Elijah," sputtered Peter. "And the other one is Moses. I'm certain of it."

Peter felt a need to celebrate. He jumped to his feet, calling out to Jesus, "Lord, it is good for us to be here! If you wish, let us make three tabernacles. One for you, one for Moses and one for Elijah."

Suddenly, the shining cloud grew a hundred times brighter. A commanding voice spoke.

"This is my beloved Son, in whom I am well pleased. Listen to him!"

This was too much for the apostles. Terrified, they fell to the ground.

Then Jesus knelt beside them, saying, "Get up. Don't be afraid."

 CHAPTER **33**

A chilling wind blew off the Galilean hills. As Jesus and the twelve entered Capernaum, they greeted a family departing for Jerusalem, where they would soon celebrate the Feast of Tabernacles and Yom Kippur, the Day of Atonement.

When they entered the village, Jesus parted from his disciples to visit his mother and half brothers. But when he arrived at his brothers' home, a sense of discomfiture hung over the meal table.

"We are preparing to leave for the Feast," James his half brother said to Jesus. "We are glad you're here and able to travel with us."

Jesus said nothing. He had been quiet all evening.

"All good Jews will be in Jerusalem. There will be many who have not yet heard you speak."

Jesus ate in silence. James grew frustrated.

"What good are signs and wonders in the small villages of Galilee? If you can really do the things they say you do, go to Jerusalem and show yourself to the world!"

Jesus smiled reassuringly, saying, "You go ahead. I do not plan to go up to Jerusalem, for my time has not yet come."

His brothers were concerned for his safety, but they did not press him. The following day, the family left for Jerusalem.

The apostles and Jesus stayed in Capernaum for the next two days, while rain drizzled steadily. Then Jesus announced to the twelve, "We are going to Jerusalem. We will travel in secret by way of Samaria."

The Feast of Tabernacles was the grandest of all Jewish celebrations. Small dwellings covered by tree branches were erected all over Jerusalem, in the streets and on rooftops. Many went outside the city to live in them during the feast; they did this to remember how the children of Israel had lived for forty years during their wilderness wanderings.

On the last day of the weeklong festival, immediately after sunrise, the people left their booths to take part in a celebration at the Temple.

To the accompaniment of flutes, the priests shouted, "Praise the Lord. Praise, O servants of the Lord, praise the name of the Lord!"

The people responded by shaking their myrtle and willow branches toward the altar and shouting, "*Hallelu Yah*" which means "Praise the Lord!"

The priests shouted, "Oh, give thanks to the Lord, for he is good!"

The people responded, "For his mercy endures forever!"

The recitation of psalms ended when the priests shouted, "O Lord, work now salvation! O Lord, send us prosperity!" Then the people waited in awesome silence for God, to hear their prayer.

It was in this momentous silence that Jesus of Nazareth stepped out of the crowd, as if in answer to their prayer, and called: "IF ANYONE IS THIRSTY, LET HIM COME TO ME AND DRINK! Whoever believes in me shall have rivers of living water flowing from within him," he said.

A murmur spread through the crowd. Some were frightened by the authority with which Jesus spoke; some were hostile toward him; many were thirsty for God and believed in his words.

The Temple guards were paralyzed. They stood amazed at his message, unsure whether to take action or not.

CHAPTER **34**

On the Monday after the feast, the fields around Jerusalem were littered with branches and leaves from the discarded booths. Before the sun came up, Jesus was in the temple to worship, but even at daybreak the people were drawn to him. A few hundred gathered around him as he sat to teach. The Pharisees and priests remained at a distance, with a conspiratorial air.

Then a woman's cry was heard outside the gates.

"No! No!" The protests and shouts grew until two Pharisees appeared, dragging a disheveled woman. A pack of scribes and Sadducees followed, barking, "Guilty! Guilty!" The woman's eyes were wide with panic. She was thrown onto the pavement in front of Jesus.

One of the Pharisees announced smugly to Jesus, "This woman was caught in adultery. "The Law of Moses commands that we stone her." He looked about him with a sneer. "But what do you say?"

The authorities were well aware of this woman's affair and had been waiting for just the right moment to serve her up to the healer from Nazareth. With a crowd of witnesses present, her sin would pose a prickly dilemma for Jesus.

"Everyone knows the Law," an elder Pharisee had reasoned. "If a man and woman lie together in adultery, they are to be stoned. If this Jesus is from God, he cannot deny God's Law."

"But Rome has taken away our authority to stone sinners," said another, "Only a Roman court can condemn a person to death."

"Precisely!" said another. "If Jesus says, 'Stone her,' he will be arrested for murder and inciting a riot. Then he will be Rome's problem. And if he says, 'Stone her,' where then is his gospel of forgiveness?"

The woman wondered, the Pharisees wondered, the people wondered: *What will Jesus say?*

But Jesus said nothing. Instead, he bent to scribble in the dust with his finger.

The Pharisees began to grow uncomfortable.

"Moses commanded that we stone adulterers. What is your verdict?"

Jesus looked into the faces of the Pharisees. His quiet pronouncement was heard by all: "Let he among you who has never sinned throw the first stone."

The silent crowd refused to move. Jesus stooped to continue writing.

After a few moments of embarrassment, the oldest Pharisee turned to leave. One by one, the Pharisees slipped away. Jesus stood to look around. Seeing none of the religious leaders, he said to the woman, "Where are the people who accuse you? Has no one condemned you?"

"No one, sir," she said. "They've all gone."

"Then neither do I condemn you," Jesus said. "Go and sin no more."

CHAPTER **3 5**

Jesus and his apostles left Jerusalem and traveled across the Jordan River to Perea. News of his confrontation in the Temple spread before him, and the crowds turned out in droves to hear Jesus speak.

Wherever he traveled now, tax collectors, sinners and outcasts flocked to Jesus. For the first time, they heard that God deeply cared about their lives. The rabbinical interpretations of the Law made it impossible to measure up to the letter of the Law. In contrast to the Pharisees, Jesus preached that their Father would gladly welcome them into his kingdom, if only they would repent and believe in his Son.

Two months after the Feast of Tabernacles, Jesus once again returned to Jerusalem for *Chanukkah*, "the festival of lights." Concerned for his safety, Peter and John attempted to dissuade Jesus, but he would not be deterred.

Winter had come to Jerusalem, and a cold fog settled over the area. Jesus was bundled with an extra tunic when he walked onto the porches of the Temple. Immediately, the people surged to him, barring his way.

A spokesman of the people asked, "How long will you keep us in suspense? Tell us plainly if you are the Messiah."

With remarkable forbearance, Jesus said, "The miracles I do in my Father's name speak for me, but you do not believe."

"And why can we not understand your sayings?" the man asked.

"You are not my sheep, therefore you do not understand my words. My sheep hear my voice, and they follow me. I give them eternal life, and they shall never perish."

"Blasphemy!" a priest yelled from the fringes of the crowd. "Silence him! Don't let him speak blasphemy in the Temple!"

The crowd began yelling and taking up stones.

Lifting his hands, Jesus spoke quietly, "I have shown you many good works of my Father. For which of these miracles do you stone me?"

"We do not stone you for miracles," replied a priest, "but for blasphemy! Because you are a mere man who claims to be God!"

"If I do not do the works of my Father, then don't believe me. But if I do miracles, believe the miracles, so that you may know that the Father is in me, and I am in him."

"No!" The crowd erupted. "Stone the blasphemer!"

But Jesus turned his back to the crowd and walked toward the gate. He did not look back, nor was he afraid they would try to harm him, for he knew it was not yet his hour to die.

CHAPTER **36**

Flames crackled from the small fire. Jesus and the twelve huddled around the flame for warmth. They had tarried in the cold highlands of the Moab hills for what seemed all winter, though they had been there but a few weeks.

"Someone is coming!" James the Less whispered. The apostles stood to meet the stranger.

Jesus immediately recognized him as the servant of Mary of Magdala, and of Martha and Lazarus, Mary's brother and sister.

"Lazarus is sick." The servant spoke anxiously to Jesus. "Mary and Martha ask that you come immediately."

The twelve glanced nervously at one another. The apostles knew and loved Lazarus and his sisters, but a return to Judea was ill advised. The people of Jerusalem had tried to stone Jesus. If the Jewish leaders caught wind of the fact that he was within their borders, they would likely try to arrest him.

"This sickness will not end in death," Jesus told the servant. "Lazarus is sick for the glory of God,"

"What shall I tell Mary and Martha?" the servant inquired.

"Tell them that God's Son will be glorified through this."

During the next two days, Jesus did not mention Lazarus but explained to his apostles that soon it would be necessary for him to go to Jerusalem. There he would suffer at the hands of the authorities, be crucified, and on the third day rise again. The apostles did not understand.

After the two days had passed, Jesus awakened the twelve early in the morning. "Get up," he urged. "We are going to Bethany."

Nearly every Jew experienced some level of holy excitement when approaching Jerusalem, but there was no excitement in the hearts of the twelve this day. As they drew near Bethany, one of the apostles instructed a boy to run ahead to Mary's house to tell them Jesus was coming.

Shortly, Martha came running and fell at Jesus' feet. Without greeting him, she blurted out, "Oh, Lord! If only you had been here my brother would not have died."

Lazarus had already been dead four days.

Jesus, smiling, said, "Your brother will rise again."

Martha stood, trying to muster her strength, and said, "I know he shall rise again in the resurrection at the last day."

But Jesus had more immediate plans. "I am the resurrection and the life," he said to her. "Whoever lives and believes in me will never die."

He placed his hands on her shoulders to ask, "Do you believe this?"

Martha answered him, saying, "I believe that you are the Christ . . . the Son of God, who was to come into the world."

Jesus smiled and nodded, as Martha ran off to tell her sister.

Soon Mary came hurrying down the path toward Jesus.

"Lord, if you had been here my brother would not have died," Mary fell at Jesus' feet and began to weep.

Jesus, deeply moved by her grief, asked, "Where have you laid him?"

They walked into a narrow valley with limestone caves. Many of these caves had been fashioned into tombs. As Jesus approached the tomb of Lazarus, a crowd convened. As Jesus surveyed those gathered, he realized that no one there truly understood he held life in his hands.

Jesus wept.

Someone in the crowd saw his tears and said, "See how Jesus loved Lazarus!"

"Take away the stone," Jesus commanded, and four young men quickly rolled it away. Through the dark shadows, the corpse could be seen.

Then Jesus lifted his face to pray, "Father, I pray for the benefit of the people standing here, that they may believe you sent me."

Then with a loud voice, Jesus shouted: "Lazarus . . . come forth!"

The body wrapped in linen sat up. Quickly, several young men and apostles ran to Lazarus, unwrapping the cloths that had been wound about his body.

The elders who had officiated at the burial of Lazarus knew he had been dead. They hurried to nearby Jerusalem to alert the authorities. "Jesus is a threat," they declared. "Many among our people are ready to follow him."

So the priests and the Pharisees called a meeting. After much deliberation, one stood and spoke. "If we let him go on like this, everyone will believe in him. And when the Romans hear of the people uniting behind this man, the soldiers will take both our authority and our nation."

"If Jesus whips the crowd into a frenzy and they should attack the Roman soldiers," another cautioned, "we will all perish!"

Caiaphas, the high priest, called them to order. Far better that they execute a blameless man, he claimed, than to await the certain slaughter of multitudes by the soldiers. Therefore, he said, Jesus should be eliminated.

While people in Jerusalem were buzzing over the resurrection in Bethany, Jesus and his disciples headed north through the hill country. From there, many went into Galilee to spread the news that Jesus was coming. A multitude gathered to him in this place, and Jesus remained there until Passover. Then he set his face like a flint toward Jerusalem, knowing this would be his final journey.

CHAPTER **3 7**

In the days leading to the feast of Passover, the word on the streets was that the chief priest planned to arrest Jesus if he dared to show himself in Jerusalem. Because of this, many said, "Jesus will not come to Jerusalem. It is too dangerous for him here." Others argued that if Jesus were truly the Messiah, he had nothing to fear.

The Pharisees and priests fully expected the Nazarene to come, and were prepared to seize him before he could enter the Temple. "If anyone knows where he is staying," the priests told their spies, "report it immediately so that we might arrest him."

Early Sunday morning, the day after the Sabbath, many of his followers went ahead of Jesus into Jerusalem to spread news of his coming.

By midday, thousands had gathered at the city gate to see if the one they called Messiah would indeed come to the city. The chief priests and Pharisees immediately sent representatives to observe his arrival and arrest him, if possible.

Jesus and the twelve departed Bethany at mid-morning. The mountainous path climbed the Mount of Olives, past the village of Bethphage.

As they came near to the village, Jesus instructed Peter and John, saying, "Go to the village ahead of you. Just as you enter, you will find a small donkey, a colt which no one has ever ridden. Untie it and bring it here."

Jesus said to them, "If anyone asks you, 'Why are you taking this animal?' tell him, 'The Lord has need of the donkey and will send it back.'"

As Peter and John entered the village, they spotted a young donkey. Without hesitation, they began to lead it away. The owner of the donkey ran after them, shouting, "Where are you going with my colt?"

Peter said, "The Lord has need of the donkey and will send it back shortly."

Bethphage was filled with pilgrims unable to secure lodging in Jerusalem, and the rumors of the coming Messiah had reached the colt's owner. "Jesus of Nazareth? Here?" he said excitedly. "If the Messiah needs my animal, take it with my blessing!"

Leading the donkey to Jesus, Peter and John removed their tunics to drape them over the animal for Jesus to ride upon. Jesus sat upon the colt. Resuming their ascent of Olivet, the apostles broke into a psalm of praise. "Open to me the gates of righteousness. I will go through them and praise the Lord," they sang.

Meanwhile, an enthusiastic crowd followed after Jesus. As they neared the summit of Olivet, the crowd joined with the apostles in singing.

The apostles marched victoriously, moved by the excitement of the crowd. When the procession swept over the ridge, the city of Jerusalem loomed before them.

The Roman road descended straight down Olivet, and Jesus could see that thousands of people had lined the road leading into Jerusalem to greet him. Many had spread their cloaks on the road, while others cut palm branches from the trees to spread on the road in his honor.

The crowds ahead of him picked up the refrain of those that followed, shouting, "Hosanna to the Son of David! Blessed is he who comes in the name of the Lord!"

The apostles were caught up in the excitement and did not notice that Jesus was untouched by the enthusiasm. A single tear fell down his face as he stared at the city that had rejected him. Jesus said quietly, "O Jerusalem, if you only knew . . . . The day will come when your enemies will trample down your walls, because you did not recognize the time of God's coming to you."

The Pharisees who had been sent out with the crowd from Jerusalem were caught up in the surge of the multitudes.

There was no chance they could arrest Jesus when he was surrounded by so many supporters. Still, one of them forced his way into the road to confront Jesus. With agitation in his voice, he said, "Teacher, rebuke your disciples! They are out of control!"

Jesus now broke from his reverie and smiled broadly. He looked down on the Pharisee and said, laughing, "If they were to keep quiet, the stones would cry out in their place."

Jesus rode the donkey through the gate and into the narrow streets of the city. There he dismounted and looked about him as the people cheered ever louder. Within days, these who worshiped him would turn fickle and shout for his death. But today their voices would not be silenced.

CHAPTER **38**

Early Tuesday morning, as Jesus walked again toward Jerusalem from Bethpage, where he had spent the night, the people swarmed about him. Jesus led the procession to the Temple and went immediately to Solomon's Porch, a place where scholars and teachers of the Law often debated. Jesus sat to teach there, and the people rushed to claim seats.

The priests would have arrested him then and there if they could have, but they feared the wrath of the multitudes. So they left him to his teaching and went away to plot.

Later, the priests sent the Pharisees and Herodians with a question they felt would entangle Jesus, and perhaps get him in trouble with the Roman authorities.

"Teacher," they said, "we know that you teach the way of God in accordance with the truth. Tell us then your opinion. Is it right to pay taxes to Caesar? Should we as Jews pay taxes, or shouldn't we?"

If they could get Jesus to advocate withholding the tax, they could have him arrested by Roman soldiers for fomenting rebellion. Or if he said they must pay the taxes, he would alienate his followers.

Jesus shook his head and said to them, "You hypocrites! Why are you trying to trap me? Bring me the coin used for paying the tax."

A Herodian produced a Roman coin. Jesus didn't take the coin but asked, "Whose portrait is on this coin? And whose inscription?"

"Caesar's," the man answered. "Tiberius Caesar, son of Augustus."

Jesus smiled, then answered, "Give to Caesar the things that are Caesar's, and give to God the things that are God's."

The day was coming to an end, as was Jesus' ministry. He led his apostles out of Jerusalem.

Jesus made his way through the Kidron Valley, climbing past the Garden of Gethsemane. A flat, white limestone shelf jutted out from the grassy meadow, inviting Jesus and his apostles to rest. When they sat, Jesus looked back at Jerusalem, the City of God.

Peter pointed out the Temple, proclaiming, "Magnificent! The Temple is the most beautiful thing on earth."

But Jesus did not revel in the sight. He said to them, "Do you see those buildings? I say to you that soon every stone will be thrown down, and Jerusalem will be destroyed."

John had thought often about what Jesus had said about returning to judge the world, and wondered if his return might be connected to the destruction of Jerusalem. "What will be the sign of your coming?" he asked.

Jesus turned away from Jerusalem and spoke to them. "Take heed that no one deceives you. For many will come in my name, saying 'I am the Christ,' and will try to lead people astray. You will hear of wars and rumors of wars, but these are only the beginning of the end.

"Nation will rise against nation, kingdom against kingdom. There will be famines, epidemics and earthquakes. My followers will be tortured and killed, and they will be hated all over the world because they believe in me. Many will fall into sin and the love of many will grow cold. But those who endure to the end will be saved.

"Watch and be ready, for when you see these things, the end is near."

 CHAPTER **39**

Nervously, Judas Iscariot stood in the Temple at the place called the Court of Israel, where penitent Jews waited to offer sacrifice. Judas was uncomfortable in the presence of the enemies of his teacher.

Jesus was supposed to deliver us from the Romans, the frightened apostle told himself. Now he tells us he is going to die! *The enemies of Jesus were powerful men. If they are willing to destroy an innocent man for his teaching, what will they do to me?*

Judas had heard the priests were looking for an opportunity to arrest Jesus. He had conceived of a plan to save his own skin by handing Jesus over, and in the process make some money.

Judas had been taking money all along from the money bag. Judas had been using it to make payment on a small piece of land known as Potter's Field.

His nervousness showed as Judas whispered to a Levite official, "I must talk to your superiors about Jesus."

The Levite whisked Judas through a door and into the caucus room where the Levites were gathered. After the Jewish leaders confirmed his identity, Judas announced, "I can help you capture Jesus."

Smiles broke out all around, broadening the faces of the priests.

Judas explained his plan. "We are going to celebrate the Passover meal in Jerusalem tomorrow—the twelve of us and the teacher. After the meal, Jesus will go to pray. I will lead you to him."

One of the priests asked, smiling, "What can we do to assist you?"

What Judas wanted was money to pay off the remainder of his land. He had thought about the plan for several days—now was the time to see if it would work. "I carry the money bag for Jesus and his disciples. I am in charge of providing for the poor and indigent. What are you willing to give me for the poor if I hand Jesus over to you?"

"Will thirty pieces of silver meet their needs?" the priest asked.

Judas nodded.

The priest motioned to an aide, who instantly left the room. Shortly he returned, holding a leather sack. The priest nodded for the bag to be placed on the table in front of Judas.

Then the priest said, "The Sanhedrin counts it a privilege to contribute to the poor. May your mission successfully recapture the hope of Israel."

CHAPTER **40**

Who gets the seat of honor next to Jesus?" James the Less asked as the apostles climbed the steps toward the upper room of a private home in Jerusalem.

"Not you," Andrew said to the laughter of the others.

Peter and John busied themselves with preparations for the Passover meal.

When all had arrived, Philip announced, "The twelve are all here, Lord."

The apostles milled about, reluctant to take the honored seat next to Jesus. But Jesus settled the matter by saying, "Judas, you sit to my left. John, you shall be at my right."

A broad smile broke through Judas' black beard. The apostles approved of the selection of Judas; he was respected for his ability to manage the money.

"Sit wherever you like," Jesus said to the others. They chose their seats.

"I have desired to eat this Passover meal with you before I suffer," Jesus said. Then he took a cup, saying, "Blessed are you, Lord our God, who has created the fruit of the vine!"

Jesus rose to retrieve the pitcher and basin, then brought them to the table. The apostles glanced at one another, uncertain as to what they were supposed to do.

Jesus knelt before Judas Iscariot . . . and washed his feet in the basin. Then he dried them with the towel which was around his waist. From his knees, Jesus looked up into Judas' eyes, looking for repentance. But all Jesus saw was arrogance.

When Jesus knelt where Simon Peter sat, the big fisherman leapt to his feet and shouted, "Lord, why are you going to wash my feet?"

"If I do not wash you," Jesus answered, "you'll have no part with me."

"Then, Lord," Peter tried to make amends, "do not wash only my feet, but my hands and my head as well!"

Jesus washed the feet of each of the twelve. The apostles sat stunned by the act of humility.

"Do you understand what I have done for you?" Jesus asked. "You have called me 'teacher' and 'Lord,' and rightly so, for that is who I am. Since I am your teacher and have washed your feet, you ought to wash one another's feet. I have given you this example to follow.

"No servant is greater than his master, nor is a messenger greater than the one who sent him.

"Though I have washed you, not all of you are clean," Jesus said. "One of you is going to betray me this night."

Several of them, including Judas, shook their heads in denial. But amid the hubbub Judas leaned over to his teacher to whisper, "Teacher, is it I?"

The apostles saw anguish in the face of Jesus. John leaned against his shoulder and whispered, "Lord, who is it?"

Jesus would not openly accuse Judas. Knowing this was the Father's will, Jesus would do nothing to halt the chain of events that had been set in motion. So he announced, "The one who will betray me is the one to whom I will give the bread after I dip it in the stew."

Sitting before him was a large bowl of lamb stew. According to tradition, the master of the feast took the unleavened bread, broke it and dipped it into the stew, then served the guest of honor. So no one saw anything out of the ordinary when Jesus broke off a morsel of bread, dipped it into the stew and handed it to Judas. None—except Judas—recognized the sign of which Jesus had spoken.

Guilt and shame flooded his soul, but he shook off his guilt to smile, and raised the bread to the other apostles in a toasting gesture. At that moment, he surrendered his soul to Satan, and his heart turned black.

Jesus whispered to him, "What you have to do—do quickly."

Judas arose, his face stone hard. Without looking back, he snatched the bag of money that belonged to the apostles. Then he slipped out the door.

Peter said to his brother Andrew, "Where is Judas going?" Andrew said, "He had the money bag with him. Perhaps he has gone for more provisions for the feast. Or maybe he's gone to buy for the poor."

After they had finished eating, Jesus stood and took a portion of unleavened bread he had set aside earlier. He blessed the bread and broke it, saying, "'Take this and eat. This is my body which is broken for you. Do this in remembrance of me."

The bread was passed from man to man, each taking a portion and eating.

According to custom, the cup of blessing was filled at the close of the supper. Jesus took this cup, lifted it heavenward and gave thanks. Then he looked around at the men who followed him and said, "This cup is the new covenant in my blood, which is poured out for the forgiveness of sins. As often as you drink it, you will remember me."

Jesus handed the cup to Andrew. And each apostle drank. Then he taught them one last time before his death. "My children, I will be with you only a little longer, then I must go away.

"A new commandment I give to you: Love one another as I have loved you. By this all men will know that you are my disciples."

Peter couldn't keep quiet any longer. "Lord, where are you going?"

"Where I am going, you cannot follow. You will follow later," Jesus said.

"Why can't I follow? I will lay down my life for you!" Jesus let Peter's words echo in the upper chamber, then said, "I tell you now, you will deny me three times this night before the rooster crows!"

Peter was shocked. "Even if I have to die with you, I will never disown you!" he declared.

Jesus shook his head, saying, "Peter, Satan would sift you like wheat. This very night you will fall away. But when you have turned back to me, you will strengthen your brothers."

"Do not let your hearts be troubled," Jesus said to the others. "In my Father's house are many mansions, and I am going there to prepare a place for you. Then I will come back to take you with me where I am."

CHAPTER **41**

The moon refused to show itself, shrouded by dark clouds in the east. The apostles struggled to distinguish the garden path.

They knew the way because they came often with Jesus to pray in the Garden of Gethsemane. Now he strode toward the garden without a misstep, even as the apostles stumbled over stones and roots.

Off to their right appeared the vague silhouettes of a grove of olive trees. Because their gnarled trunks made excellent seats, Jesus directed the apostles, "Sit here, I will go ahead to pray." He took Peter, James and John with him, disappearing into the darkness.

It was late in the evening and the apostles were tired. They wrapped their tunics about them. Soon they were sleeping.

Deeper in the garden, Jesus spoke to his three closest disciples. "I am overwhelmed with grief," he said, "crushed almost to the point of death. Stay here and keep watch with me as I pray."

But even as Jesus walked away, the three men felt their eyes growing heavy.

About a stone's throw away, Jesus fell to his knees to pray. Visions of the cross bore down on him; he knew the intense pain and agony that awaited him on the morrow. He cried out to his Father as the darkness pressed in. *My Father . . . if it is possible, I don't want to drink this cup of suffering.*

Jesus' agony was so intense, he fell with his face to the ground, fists clenched. He repeated his plea. *Father, if you are willing, please take this cup from me.*

Then off in the distance came a low rumble. A spring storm moved down the Jordan Valley. Jesus did not see the lightning, but he heard the groan of heaven. One by one, the stars were extinguished by the clouds.

Disturbed by the distant thunder, Jesus rose and returned to where he had left Peter, James and John. There he found them sleeping soundly. He shook Peter's shoulder to ask, "Could you men not stay awake and keep watch with me for even one hour?"

The three were embarrassed and could say nothing.

"Keep alert," Jesus warned. "Watch and pray or temptation will overcome you." The need to continue in prayer overwhelmed him and he turned to walk away. Looking back, he said to them, "Your spirit is willing, but the flesh is weak. Watch and pray."

Jesus returned once more to the spot where he had knelt and prayed, *My Father, if it's not possible for this cup of suffering to be taken away unless I first drink it . . . then may your will be done.*

He knew that in the morning there would be humiliation, pain, torture and finally death, yet he yielded to the Father's plan. He would have to go through the cross to get back to heaven.

Jesus heard the sound of snoring and went again to his disciples. "Why can't you keep your eyes open?" he asked, but none of them moved.

Again, collapsing under the load of grief, Jesus fell to the ground. Clutching his fists and tightening every muscle, Jesus struggled with fear. Satan his adversary gloated over the prostrate form of Jesus, certain that victory was at hand. Then an angel came to Jesus and renewed his strength, and Satan withdrew.

After a time, Jesus gathered himself and returned to his three most trusted disciples. They were asleep.

Jesus heard the voices of men coming down the road. A parade of torches and lanterns could be seen through the trees.

Jesus recognized the voice of Judas amid the talking and clamor. "The one I kiss is the man you want. Arrest him," came the voice.

"Why are you still sleeping?" Jesus awakened Peter, James and John. "Look, my hour is here, and the Son of Man is betrayed."

Judas led a gathering of Roman soldiers, Temple guards, chief priests and Levites. When the mob reached the clearing, they saw Jesus with Peter, James and John. *Is this the man?* they thought. They looked beyond him to see three fishermen, one of whom was carrying a sword.

Then Judas gave the signal. Stepping forward to embrace Jesus, he said, "Greetings, Rabbi!" Then he kissed Jesus on the cheek.

"A kiss, Judas?" Jesus looked into his conscience. "How can you betray the Son of Man with a kiss?"

The silence now broken, Peter stepped forward. "Lord, should we fight?" In one swift motion, Peter slashed at one of the servants of the high priest. But he missed the center of his head, only cutting off his ear.

"Stop!" Jesus called, cutting off the man's screams. No one moved as he picked up the ear and replaced it to the head of the servant. When Jesus removed his hand, the ear was restored.

Then he rebuked Peter, saying, "Put your sword back in its place, for all who live by the sword shall die by the sword. Don't you know I can call on my Father, who will put at my disposal twelve legions of angels?"

Then Jesus turned to the priests. "Do you think I am some dangerous criminal? Am I leading a rebellion, that you come with swords and clubs?"

There was no answer. A priest turned and nodded at the soldiers and they stepped toward Jesus. Jesus stepped forward to meet the soldiers, returning their glare with a look of love. He asked, "Who is it you want?"

"Jesus of Nazareth," the captain replied.

"I am he," came his simple response. And as he said this, the soldiers were driven backwards to the ground, as if they had been standing on a chariot when the horse bolted into a run, throwing them backwards.

"Who are you looking for?" Jesus repeated his question, as the soldiers righted themselves.

"I told you that I am he," Jesus said. "If you are looking for me, then let the men who are with me go."

The captain looked to the chief priest, who answered, "We have no interest in them . . . at this time."

One by one, the apostles slipped away into the darkness.

CHAPTER **42**

The tramp of Roman troops echoed through the streets of Jerusalem in the early morning hours of Friday, just after midnight. Levitical guards from the Temple followed after the soldiers.

Annas was the power behind the office of the high priest, even though Rome had removed him from office because he would not fully cooperate with them. In Annas' place, Rome had appointed his son-in-law, Caiaphas. But the Jews still considered Annas God's instrument.

Dawn was coming, and Annas and the priests needed to agree on a charge that would be lodged against Jesus. Because the Romans did not allow Jewish officials to exercise capital punishment, only the Romans could execute Jesus. Therefore, the charge must be worthy of swift execution. But when Annas interrogated Jesus regarding his teachings, Jesus would not answer his questions.

"I have spoken openly to the world," Jesus replied. "Ask those who heard me. Surely they know what I said."

When Jesus said this, one of the Temple guards struck him in the face. "Is this the way you answer a high priest?"

"If I have said something evil," Jesus said, "then tell me what evil I have spoken. But if I spoke the truth, then why do you strike me?"

Annas had heard enough. Any official charges would have to be made by his son-in-law Caiaphas and the Sanhedrin anyway, so Annas sent Jesus to Caiaphas' palace.

As the Temple guard led Jesus, bound, toward Caiaphas' quarters, Peter and the youngest apostle John fell in behind the procession. At Caiaphas' house, the Temple guard entered with Jesus, but the woman at the door kept the others out.

John recognized the girl and approached her, saying, "You know me. My father is Zebedee who sells fish to Caiaphas." She allowed John to enter the house, while Peter waited in the courtyard. Caiaphas was jittery, high-strung, explosive. As Jesus was brought in, the high priest babbled, "I have you now, Galilean! Your fate is in my hands."

But although Caiaphas wanted to summarily order an execution, Rome had taken the death penalty from the Jews. He could excommunicate Jesus, but what good was that? He would gladly kill Jesus with his bare hands, but his position wouldn't allow him.

Upon entering the courtyard, Peter gravitated toward the red glow of a charcoal fire. Several bearded men huddled around to warm their faces. Peter attempted to blend in with the men, appearing to be indifferent to what was going on. Then he was spotted by the young woman at the door. "You were with Jesus of Nazareth, the man they have on trial upstairs."

"Not me," Peter protested. "I don't know him."

Confusion reigned upstairs in the palace. Dawn was rapidly approaching, and those gathered in the second floor chamber couldn't agree on a charge to bring against Jesus.

Proof was needed if any charge was to hold water with the Roman governor, Pontius Pilate. Many council members knew someone who could bring charges against Jesus, some of whom would accept payment to make false accusations. Quickly, servants were dispatched to find those witnesses.

Members of the Sanhedrin tried to coerce their servants to give testimony. But it didn't work. First one man would speak out against Jesus, then another would contradict his story.

Jesus stood in silence. Caiaphas fidgeted in his seat.

Since the servants and false witnesses could not get their stories straight, some of the members of the Sanhedrin brought charges against Jesus. One of the council members stepped forward, charging, "This fellow said that he was able to destroy the Temple and build it again within three days."

Nervous laughter filled the room. They all had heard about this claim.

"His violent hands have been raised against the Temple of God!" the council member continued.

Caiaphas seized the opportunity to cross examine Jesus. "What do you say to this charge?"

When Jesus did not answer, Caiaphas demanded: "Tell me who you are!"

Jesus answered, "Ask your witnesses. They know what I said."

Caiaphas jumped to his feet, waving frantically. "I demand by the Living God: Tell us whether you are the Christ, the Son of God!"

As the echoes died, Jesus responded, "Yes, it is as you say. One day you will see the Son of Man sitting at the right hand of the Mighty One on the clouds of heaven."

"Blasphemy!" the high priest cried. "This is blasphemy!"

The Sanhedrin knew the law, that if one were pronounced guilty he could be tried on the same day, but not punished on that same day. However, in the case of blasphemy, the offender could be judged immediately.

"Put him to death!" the high priest screamed at the top of his voice. "We'll charge him with blasphemy before Pilate."

The crowd muttered their agreement, and Caiaphas asked, "What think you, gentlemen? For life?"

Silence.

"For death?"

"For death!" the priests cried.

"Then we shall recommend this sentence to our friend Pilate."

Peter sat by the wall, despairing. He had heard the cry "For death!" from the upper chamber.

Then out of the darkness stepped a Temple guard, a cousin to Malchus, the young priest whose ear Peter had cut off. He challenged Peter. "Didn't I see you with Jesus in the olive grove?"

"You are mistaken, sir," Peter said nervously. "I do not know the man."

Within the same hour, another guard stood with Peter by the fire, saying to his comrades, "Certainly this fellow was with him, for he is a Galilean." Then he said to Peter, "You are a Galilean. Your accent gives you away!"

"I tell you, I do not know the man!" Peter blurted out. He vowed an oath to God that he did not know Jesus.

At that moment, Jesus was led down the stairs and into the courtyard. Jesus glanced over at Peter, and their eyes met. Even before the tears came to Peter's eyes, a heaving sob welled up within him. He rushed out the front gate and into the darkness.

In the distance, a rooster crowed.

CHAPTER **43**

In the early morning light, a parade marched from the palace of Caiaphas to the fortress of Antonia. Jesus was dragged relentlessly through the streets. The leather straps binding his wrists ripped at his skin, while the stone streets scraped the flesh from his ankles and knees.

The few members of the Sanhedrin who accompanied the procession refused to enter the doors of Antonia. Their entrance into any heathen dwelling made them Levitically "unclean" for one day, and there were Passover sacrifices to be made later. Instead they sent word to Pontius Pilate, the Roman governor, to meet them at the front of the fortress.

"What is the charge against this man?" Pilate demanded.

Despite his bluster, Pilate was a consummate politician. Unlike the iron Roman laws he enforced, his ego allowed him to be swayed by public opinion. And only a few days earlier, opinion seemed to favor Jesus.

When the Jewish leaders did not answer immediately, Pilate bellowed, "What charges are you bringing against this man? I presume he has committed some crime."

"If he were not a criminal, we would not have brought him to you," a priest said, evading the question.

Pilate was not surprised by the Sanhedrin's reluctance to bring a direct accusation against Jesus. He knew they were hoping to force him to do their dirty work for them.

"Take him and judge him according to your Jewish laws," he said. Pilate didn't want to deal with Jesus. But the priests were persistent.

"He has committed a capital offense, and it is not lawful for us to put any man to death," they reminded Pilate.

"What has Rome to do with this man?" Pilate shot back.

The priests were dumbfounded. "You assigned soldiers from your garrison for his arrest. He has claimed to be the Christ, whom the people believe will lead a rebellion against Rome, so we have found him guilty of blasphemy."

Pilate snorted. He turned sharply and marched into Antonia's judgment hall. There Pilate faced the bruised and battered Jesus.

"Are you the king of the Jews?" Pilate sneered.

"My kingdom is not of this world," Jesus answered. "If my kingdom were of this world, my subjects would deliver me."

"You are a king, then!" Pilate perked up at this.

"You are right in saying I am a king," Jesus said. "I was born to be a king. I came into the world to bear witness of the truth. Everyone who sides with the truth will hear me."

Weary of the political games his position demanded he play with his own superiors and with the Jewish leaders, Pilate snorted and said, "What is truth?"

Rising from his judgment seat, Pilate walked out to the porch where a large crowd had gathered. Pilate announced, "I find no basis for a charge against this man."

An angry murmur went up from the crowd. Pilate quickly reassessed his decision and decided that the winds of opinion had shifted. Then he hit on a clever idea. It was the custom at Passover for the governor to grant amnesty to one prisoner— a prisoner of the people's choosing.

There was in prison a man called Barabbas. Barabbas, who had once taken part in a planned rebellion, had become a thief. Whatever the people might think of Jesus, everyone hated Barabbas.

Pilate said to the crowd, "It is your custom for me to release one prisoner at Passover. Who do you want me to release: Barabbas, or Jesus?"

There was a moment of stunned silence, for the crowd had not expected this choice. They had been recruited by the priests merely to shout down anyone who would voice support for the Nazarene teacher.

"Well, shall I release the 'king of the Jews'?" Pilate asked again.

"No!" one of the chief priests shouted. "Not Jesus! Barabbas!"

The crowd took their cue from the priest, shouting, "Barabbas! Barabbas!"

"What shall I do, then, with Jesus your Messiah?" Pilate asked.

"Crucify him!" the priests shouted. "Why? What crime has he committed?"

But the priests goaded the crowd to shout, "Crucify him!"

When Pilate saw that he was getting nowhere, he called for a bowl of water and washed his hands in front of the crowd. "I am hereby innocent of this man's blood," he shouted. Turning to the guards, he said angrily, "Release Barabbas!"

Furious, the Roman governor stalked back into the judgment hall. Without looking at the already bloodied form of the man they called Jesus, Pilate said to his soldiers, "Flog him."

CHAPTER **44**

Jesus was dragged into the belly of Antonia. The Roman guards hooked the thongs binding his wrists to a beating post, extending his arms above his head. They ripped his tunic to the waist, and the olive skin of his back was revealed.

A soldier took hold of a cat-o'-nine-tails, a leather whip of nine thongs.

"ONE!" A centurion yelled out as the guard laid the first stripes on Jesus' back. But there was no sound from Jesus.

"TWO!" came the second command. No sound from Jesus.

"THREE!" Still no sound from Jesus.

The lashes reached thirty-nine. "If he dies with thirty-nine stripes," was the common refrain, "then it proves he was guilty." But the scourging didn't kill Jesus. It merely humiliated and tortured him.

The soldiers loosed the knot in the straps about his wrists, and Jesus crumbled in a heap. One of the soldiers draped a scarlet robe across his swollen back. Then they twisted together a crown of thorns and set it on his head. They placed a reed in his right hand, pretending it was a royal scepter. Then, bowing before him in mockery, one of the soldiers said, "Hail, king of the Jews," and the others laughed.

Dragging Jesus up the stairs into the judgment hall, the soldiers threw him onto the floor before Pilate. Rising from his breakfast, Pilate walked around Jesus, who was a pitiful sight.

Perhaps, Pilate thought, the indignities this man had suffered would appease the priests. So he took Jesus by the arm and drew him to the porch.

"Behold the man," Pilate called for all to hear. "I have brought him out to show you what you have done and to let you know once more that I find no basis for a charge against him."

And the chief priests and Pharisees took up the shout once more: "Crucify him! Nail him to the cross!"

Pilate said to them, "*You* crucify him! I find no fault in him." The Jewish leaders had not expected the Roman governor to be so squeamish. Frustrated, the priests announced, "We have a law, and according to that law he must die, because he claimed to be the Son of God."

But this did not move Pilate. Jesus had not broken any Roman law, only their Jewish traditions. Pilate pondered his dilemma. He took Jesus inside and demanded of him, "Don't you realize I have the power either to free you or to crucify you?"

Then Jesus answered him, saying, "You would have no power over me if it were not given to you from above."

When Pilate returned to the porch, the spokesman for the chief priests shouted, "If you let this man go, you are no friend of Caesar. Anyone who claims to be a king opposes Caesar. Jesus of Nazareth has set himself to be king, and that is treason!" Pilate could not ignore this line of reasoning.

"Shall I then crucify your king?" Pilate cried out to the leaders.

"We have no king but Caesar," they answered.

Pilate knew the Jews' long-standing hatred of Roman rule. Their hatred for this Galilean must run even deeper. He handed Jesus over to be crucified.

CHAPTER **45**

The scarlet robe was torn off Jesus' body, causing his wounds to bleed afresh. He was led out of the fortress toward the hill called Golgotha—Calvary in Greek—which means the Place of the Skull.

A centurion led a detachment of four men, a hammer swinging menacingly from his belt. The soldiers made sure the victim carried his own instrument of execution—a wooden cross. But after the scourging, Jesus was too weak to carry his load. He continually fell. "Up!" one of the soldiers cried again and again, each time beating Jesus with a rope.

Behind Jesus came two thieves, each carrying his own cross. Following close behind was John, the only apostle who hadn't run away.

Word of these happenings had reached many who believed Jesus' teaching. Hundreds of weeping men and women now lined the street, mingling with his detractors.

A wooden shingle was placed around Jesus' neck; later it would be nailed to the top of the cross. On the shingle Pilate had written, "JESUS OF NAZARETH, THE KING OF THE JEWS."

After Jesus had fallen several times along the route, the Roman soldiers didn't waste time beating him again.

"You!" the centurion yelled to a man in the crowd.

Simon, a pilgrim from the land of Cyrene, was dressed differently; his dark green robe and red tunic stood out in the crowd of white and brown tunics. "Pick up that cross and follow us."

So Simon the Cyrenian hefted the cross onto his shoulder and carried it for Jesus to the place called Golgotha.

The heavy timbers made a cracking sound as Simon dropped the cross at the top of the hill. Calloused hands stripped the sandals, cloak and tunic from Jesus and stretched him on the timbers. Ropes tied his hands and feet to the cross. Then a Roman soldier, swinging a large wooden mallet, approached Jesus. This muscular man took a black iron spike, placed it in the palm of Jesus' right hand and with a mighty swing of his hammer, began driving the spike into the timber.

THWAPPP . . . , the sound rang out. THWAPPP . . . THWAPPP. . . The soldiers didn't pay any attention—they had heard the sound may times.

Next, the executioner turned to Jesus' other hand, repeating the process. He lifted the hammer. THWAPPP. . . THWAPPP. . . THWAPPP. . .

He did the same to the feet of Jesus.

A hole almost two feet deep had been chiseled out of the limestone. With Jesus nailed to the cross, the soldiers put their huge shoulders to the weight. Slowly they lifted the cross skyward. The weight of Jesus' body caused the nails in his hands and feet to rip his flesh. His body screamed in agony, but he said nothing. The soldiers raised the cross until it was nearly upright. Then the executioner kicked it so that the base of the cross dropped into the hole.

THUMP! Jesus shut his eyes as his body shook with pain, but he said nothing for a moment. Then he lifted his eyes to heaven in prayer, "Father, forgive them, for they know not what they do." It was nine o'clock in the morning.

The well-dressed man was frantic. He pushed his way through the crowd streaming out of the Temple.

CHAPTER **46**

"I have sinned . . . ," Judas panted in a low voice. "Get out of my way!"

I have sinned! he thought. *I must see the priests now!*

One of the priests recognized Judas and opened a side door to him. Judas fought his way in and ran toward the caucus room, where he had made his deal with the enemies of Jesus. He came face to face with a knot of laughing priests.

"You must stop this execution!" Judas demanded.

But they laughed all the harder. "You have your money. Take your silver and go."

But Judas had to cleanse his soul. With a hoarse cry, he sobbed, "I have sinned . . . I am doomed to hell!"

The priests laughed. They had no words of mercy for Judas.

Judas glared wildly, his chest heaving with anger and sorrow. Then he untied the bag holding the thirty pieces of silver, removed a coin and turned it over in his hand. He ran out the door toward the sanctuary of the Temple.

"Wait!" the priests shouted. They could not allow him to do what it appeared he might do.

Judas ran wildly toward the Court of Israel. It was there that penitent worshipers would wait while the priests offered sacrifice of forgiveness for them. With a mad cry, he hurled the thirty pieces of silver onto the marble pavement, yelling, "I have sinned! I need forgiveness!"

Before the priests could reach him, Judas fled the Temple and ran down into the valley.

Judas crossed the valley, frantically climbing up the steep ascent to the place called Potter's Field. Around its edge, cliffs dropped into the valley. The cliffs were lined with jagged rocks.

Judas was heading to a gnarled tree that grew there—a tree that extended from the cliff out over the valley. There Judas knelt to untie his sash.

For the past day, his mind had been in a storm. Now he grew calm. He had returned the silver and had asked for forgiveness. He couldn't believe it was forthcoming, however, and he knew what he must do.

Judas tied one end of the sash around his neck. Then he climbed the tree, leaning out over the precipice to attach the sash to the tree limb. The tree was visible across the Hinnom Valley, so those in the city would be able to see what he was about to do. Judas wanted his death to send a message.

Returning to the ground, Judas was ready. He stood at the edge of the cliff, looking across the valley to Jerusalem.

Then Judas jumped out over the precipice. He swung for a moment, but the knot in his sash loosened under his weight.

Judas fell onto the jagged rocks beneath. His intestines spilled out as the body bounced to the bottom of the gorge.

CHAPTER **47**

From the cross flanking Jesus to his left, the convicted thief looked down with hatred on the Roman soldiers. He screamed as he used the nails that held him to pull himself up where he could take a breath, then slumped down again as he lost consciousness. But from within the blackness, he heard the soldiers mocking Jesus.

"If you are the king of the Jews," one soldier said, "save yourself."

The soldiers laughed.

The thief at Jesus' left hand turned his sweat-blinded eyes to the center cross. "You're no king," he said to Jesus. "If you were the savior, then you could save yourself and us."

But the thief at the other hand of Jesus had seen him teach in the Temple. He had heard the guards say Pilate had found no fault in the man. He had seen the shingle that identified him as the king of the Jews, and he believed the writing. He had heard Jesus say, "Father, forgive them," and the thief was amazed.

"Don't you fear God?" he gasped. "We're going to die."

"We're thieves," his hardened cohort answered, "we deserve to die."

"But this man does not deserve to die," the other protested.

"Hah! If he's done nothing wrong, then why is he here with us?"

But the repentant thief only shook his head. He looked toward Jesus, searching for forgiveness. The thief beseeched him, "Remember me when you come into your kingdom."

Jesus smiled weakly and promised, "Today you will be with me in Paradise."

Often the victims of crucifixion would cling to life for two or three days. But John, the apostle who had watched as they crucified Jesus, did not think his master was going to last the day. So he left Golgotha to retrieve Mary, the mother of Jesus.

The beloved apostle led Mary to the foot of the cross. With them came three other women—Mary's sister, Mary the mother of James the Less and Mary of Magdala.

Without thought for himself, Jesus looked upon his mother. "Woman . . . . woman, here is your son," Jesus said, nodding at John.

Through blood-filled eyes, he gave John a final command: "Here is your mother."

Jesus was entrusting the care of his mother to the faithful apostle, and John understood. John left Golgotha with his arm around Mary, and they went to his home in Jerusalem.

 CHAPTER **4 8**

At Golgotha a frightened multitude watched as Jesus suffered. The soul of Jesus groaned, and it seemed all of creation groaned with him.

Jesus tried to open his eyes. Then arching his neck toward heaven, he cried out, "My God, why have you forsaken me?"

Within minutes the land was shrouded in darkness. The minutes passed into an hour; then two hours; then three.

A voice from the crowd cried out, "It's the end of the world! God has shut off the sun because we have crucified an innocent man!"

In the third hour of darkness, Jesus said from the cross, "I thirst . . . ."

One of the soldiers, moved with pity, went to fetch something to relieve his thirst. The soldier fastened a sponge to a three foot reed, then dipped the sponge in some sour wine. He lifted the sponge to the mouth of the dying man, and Jesus drank.

Red drops dripped from his lips as the sponge was removed. From a distance, Mary Magdalene sobbed and said, "He has tasted death for every man."

With renewed vigor, Jesus tugged at the nails holding him to the cross, pulling himself up to look to heaven. Then he cried, "It is finished!"

His work on earth—and his sufferings—were over. It was about three o'clock in the afternoon.

Finally, Jesus called out, "Father, into your hands I commit my spirit!"

The crowd's low grumblings ceased. Every eye turned to stare at him.

There was silence, then Jesus of Nazareth bowed his head. At that moment, a shudder arose, and the city of Jerusalem began to shake. For what seemed an eternity, an earthquake rumbled through the city, shaking its structural and spiritual foundations.

The veil of the Temple, the massive curtain that separated the Jewish people from the dwelling place of God, was torn in half from top to bottom by the hand of God.

CHAPTER **49**

Within a few hours the sun would set, beginning the Sabbath. Then nothing could be done about the corpse which hung on the cross, and it would remain there until the Sabbath had passed. Meanwhile, scavengers—ravens, buzzards, vultures—would desecrate the body.

The Law of Moses demanded that the body of a criminal should not be left unburied overnight, particularly during a Sabbath. To make matters worse, this was a Sabbath of the

Passover. So it was that the chief priests went to Pilate and petitioned him to hasten the deaths of those being crucified that their bodies might be buried before sundown.

So Pilate commanded that the leg bones of those crucified be broken with a club or hammer, followed by a swift stroke from a sword or lance to put an end to what remained of life. Breaking the kneecaps and legs was not meant to kill the victim; it was merely Rome's way of increasing the suffering momentarily to compensate for the merciful end which followed.

When word reached Golgotha, the centurion ordered one of his men to take the hammer and smash the kneecaps of the thief to the left of Jesus. Screams of anguish pierced the silence. The same was done to the thief to the right of the Nazarene.

But when the soldier stepped toward Jesus, the centurion restrained him. "Jesus is dead," he said to him.

The soldier shrugged and picked up his lance. He scraped the spearhead two or three times on a stone to ensure it was sharp. Then, placing the lance against the exposed side of Jesus, he put his weight against the spear, thrusting it straight into the heart of the dead man. To the astonishment of the onlookers, a sudden gush of blood and water poured out of the body.

At the fortress Antonia, Pilate granted an audience to Joseph of Arimathea, a member of the Sanhedrin and secret disciple of Jesus. Joseph had known of the plot to destroy Jesus, but he had not been informed about the early morning meeting in which Jesus was tried and convicted—probably because he had dared to express sympathy for Jesus in a recent council meeting.

When word reached Joseph of the death of Jesus, he went to Pilate and demanded the body be turned over to him.

"Why do you want the body of the Galilean?"

"Now that he is dead, I want to pay my respects to my master."

"It pleases me to offer assistance to one who would risk exposure to defy the Sanhedrin," Pilate said. "Take the body and go." Then Pilate instructed his secretary to write a letter giving Joseph authority to receive the body of Jesus.

Because of his advanced age, Joseph knew death would visit him soon. He had a few years earlier purchased a garden in an exquisite setting and ordered a new tomb be hewed from the rock there in preparation for his burial. It was the tomb of a wealthy man; but on this day he would lay there the body of a poor carpenter turned teacher from Nazareth.

Accompanied by his servants, Joseph went immediately to the centurion with his letter of permission. The cross was lowered and laid on the ground. The ropes were loosened and the cruel nails drawn out. Joseph and his servants washed the face and body of Jesus. Then they wrapped his body in linen and carried it to the garden.

It was after five o'clock when they entered the tomb.

In haste, Joseph and Nicodemus wrapped the torso and each limb in long strips of linen. A layer of myrrh and aloe was applied on the cloths, then another layer of cloths. Finally, the head was gently wrapped in a napkin.

Joseph of Arimathea and Nicodemus then exited the tomb instructing their servants to seal the tomb by rolling a flat carved stone down a designed trench until it covered the entry completely. A smaller stone was squeezed into the crack to lodge the larger stone in place.

Three women stood far off on a small hill overlooking the garden. Mary Magdalene, Salome and Mary the mother of James the Less had followed the burial party to this place. They wanted with all their hearts to run into the garden to help anoint the body, but they could not violate Jewish customs by mingling with the men.

Mary Magdalene gathered herself resolutely. "We'll come back after the Sabbath to anoint his body."

A delegation from the chief priests and Pharisees went to see Pilate. "Sir," they said, "we remember that while he was alive the deceiver Jesus claimed repeatedly, 'After three days I shall rise again.'

"We now have reason to believe that his disciples are planning to steal the body so that they may tell the people he has been raised from the dead. So we ask that you give the order for the tomb to be placed under constant guard until the third day has passed."

So the chief priests and Pharisees went and put a seal on the stone, and posted a guard of six Roman soldiers.

 ## CHAPTER **50**

First light came to Golgotha on Sunday morning, but nothing stirred there. Light had not yet pierced the deep shadows of the nearby garden where Jesus had been entombed.

It came slowly. The Roman soldiers watching in the garden did not feel it at first. Leaves on the trees began shimmering. A gentle earthquake rumbled through the garden, dislodging the small stone holding the larger stone in its place covering the opening of the tomb. The Roman seal, stamped in a handful of cement, cracked and splintered into small pieces.

Out of the darkness stepped a shining angel. The two soldiers standing guard at the tomb's entrance trembled and fell over. Before the others nearby could even detect the source of the light, the angel put his shoulder to the stone and rolled it away.

The four remaining Roman soldiers were shaken by the brilliance of the angelic being. They began to run.

"Quick! To Antonia! We must get reinforcements!" one shouted.

"No, wait!" another called. "If it is known we ran, we will be put to death."

"Let's go to the Jewish leaders," one of the guards reasoned. "We were at the tomb under their authority. And it is said they know of the supernatural."

With that, they headed toward the Temple living quarters.

The sun still had not risen when a handful of religious officials walked toward the Temple, brushing sleep from their eyes. This was an emergency.

Skeptical, they listened to the soldiers tell about the earthquake, and the heavenly being who rolled the stone away from the cave.

The leader turned to the Roman soldiers and asked, "Did you actually see this 'person' roll away the stone?"

"Yes," they answered.

"Did you actually see Jesus of Nazareth walk out of the tomb?"

"No."

"Well, then." the leader said to the Sanhedrin. "He did not rise from the dead. The body of Jesus was stolen while the guards lay sleeping."

"But . . . ." the soldier protested.

However, before the soldiers could get the words out, they were cut off by a loud CLUNK. A bag full of coins had appeared on the table before them.

"We understand that hardworking soldiers have certain needs," the Sanhedrin said. "Consider this a reward for your information."

"But . . . we will be punished for sleeping on our watch." "Pilate is our friend," the leader of the Sanhedrin said. "We will keep you out of trouble."

Once the ruling council reached agreement, they quickly spread word that his disciples had stolen the body of Jesus.

CHAPTER **5 1**

A red glare made dark shadows of the eastern hills as a group of women made their way toward the rock-hewed tomb. They had rested on the Sabbath according to Jewish Law. Now it was the third day since the burial, and they carried oils and spices to the tomb.

"Wait here," Mary Magdalene said to the other women. "The soldiers are just ahead."

Joanna and Mary the mother of James the Less did not argue. Stealthily approaching the place, Mary Magdalene parted the leaves to spy out the garden.

Nothing! she thought. She saw no soldiers, no fire, no signs of life. The tomb was open.

Quickly she surveyed the scene and concluded that the body of Jesus had been taken. Without hesitation, she ran for Peter and John.

The other two women remained in hiding until they were certain something must have happened to their friend. Fearing the worst, they made their way toward the tomb. The women were greeted by two gleaming angels.

"Do not be afraid," the first spoke. "I know you are looking for Jesus."

Petrified, the women fell to their knees.

"He has risen from the dead, just as he said he would." The angel beckoned the ladies to look. "Come in, see the place where he lay."

The women stood and looked about them at the empty tomb. Then the first angel said to them, "Go quickly and tell his disciples that Jesus is risen. Say to them, 'He will go ahead of you into Galilee. There you will see him.'"

Without conversation, the women began to run.

Even before Mary and Joanna had emerged from their hiding place, Mary Magdalene ran shouting into the home of John the disciple.

"Peter!" she yelled. "They've taken his body!"

"Wha-a-at?" Peter muttered as he stirred from heavy sleep.

"They have taken Jesus out of the tomb. I don't know where they've put him."

Peter and John grabbed their tunics and ran out the door. Peter was first, although the younger John outran him to the tomb.

John did not enter but only stooped to look in. The tomb was empty.

Within moments, Peter came trudging into the garden. He carefully looked from one end of the tomb to the other. "What does this mean?" he asked.

Without speaking, John thought, *Jesus is alive!* He closed his eyes in grateful tears.

After several minutes of rest and fanning herself, Mary rose and stumbled into the street. She found herself drawn to the tomb, not knowing why she was returning there. She had forgotten that she left her friends there, and didn't know where Peter and John might be. Wandering aimlessly through the city, she missed the women returning from the tomb. Mary's discouragement was wrapped up in her ignorance, and she didn't know what to do but return.

When she arrived at the garden, she saw two men dressed in white.

"Why are you crying?" one of the men inquired.

"They have taken my Lord away," she said, then added, "And I don't know where they have put him."

Mary became aware that someone was behind her. She turned to see a man standing there with a kind face and smiling eyes, but through her tears she did not recognize him.

The man spoke. "Woman, why are you crying? Who are you looking for?"

"They have taken away the body of my Lord," she said. "Oh, sir, if you have him, please tell me where you have put him. I will go and get him."

Then the stranger said, "Mary," and she recognized his voice. Despair began to melt away.

Lifting her tear-stained face from her hands, Mary Magdalene looked into the eyes of Jesus.

"Rabboni . . . ?" she whispered, using the affectionate Aramaic word for "teacher." A smile slowly spread across her face. She cried out in joy, "Rabboni!" and fell at his feet, clutching them frantically.

"Do not hold on to me," Jesus said to Mary, "for I have not yet returned to the Father. Now go and tell my brothers what you have seen."

 CHAPTER **52**

Throughout the afternoon that Sunday, the apostles came out of hiding to make their way into the upper room. One by one they emerged because they heard rumors that the body of Jesus had been stolen; others had heard that the women had seen angels at the tomb.

"Have you heard about Judas?" Philip asked the others. Apparently, he said, Judas had betrayed Jesus for thirty pieces of silver, then tried to return the money to the Temple.

Philip rattled the door again to make sure it was locked. He didn't want any more surprises. The ten men gathered around the table to eat, each sitting at the place where he had been sitting during the Last Supper.

Then, suddenly, Jesus was in their midst, standing at the central place at the table. "Peace be with you," he blessed them, lifting his hands.

Some of the men were startled, others terrified.

Jesus said, "Why do you have doubts?" He held out his nail-pierced hands. "See for yourself. Look at my hands and my feet!"

The apostles were amazed and overjoyed. Jesus asked, "Do you have anything here to eat?"

Left on the table was some broiled fish and honeycomb. Jesus ate the fish then the honeycomb as the apostles watched. Clearly this was no spirit; they all knew it was Jesus in the flesh.

After he ate, Jesus gave them their commission. "When people believe the message you preach concerning me, their sins will be forgiven. Where your message is not received, the sins of the people will remain with them." Then Jesus breathed on them and said, "Receive the Holy Spirit."

Immediately, the Scriptures and the teachings of Jesus became clear to them, and they were bolstered with inner strength.

Then Jesus disappeared.

CHAPTER **5 3**

Simon Peter stood alone in the courtyard of his home in Capernaum, staring wistfully at the guest house where Jesus had often slept. Where was Jesus now? Jesus had disappeared from the upper room, leaving his disciples with little more than a daunting task for which they felt ill equipped.

Peter wanted to do *something*, but felt helpless.

The evening of the Sabbath, Peter sat on an outcropping of rocks near the dock, looking south toward the beach where Jesus had first called him to be a fisher of men. Suddenly, he knew what he would do. He rushed up the road and ran into his house, where Andrew, John, James, Nathanael, Philip and Thomas sat talking.

"I am going fishing," Peter announced. "Who's going with me?"

The clouds hung low over the Sea of Galilee that evening. There was no moon, no stars—a perfect night for fishing.

"We'll fill our nets tonight!" Peter declared.

They let their nets down shallow and deep, near the shore and in the middle of the lake. But they caught nothing.

In desperation, they threw their nets among the reeds along the shore; still they caught nothing.

It was as though all the fish had fled the Sea of Galilee. When the stars in the eastern sky began to fade, the fishermen looked at one another in resignation. Dawn was coming, so they headed for shore.

But as they drew near to Capernaum, they heard a shout from the beach. "Have you caught anything?" a stranger called to them. Peter wanted to ignore him, but Andrew yelled back, "Nothing!"

"Throw your net down on the right side of the boat," the voice came.

The moment was familiar, and Peter felt his heart stir. He snapped, "Quick, pull the net out of the water! Throw it over the other side!"

Even before the net was submerged, a school of fish churned there.

"Pull!" Peter barked. "Put your back into it!"

But there were so many fish that seven strong men, straining with all their might, could not get the net into the boat.

John looked at Peter and shouted, "It's the Lord! That's Jesus on shore!"

Without thinking, Peter reached for his tunic and slipped it on. In one swift motion, he dove into the water and with long, powerful strokes began swimming toward shore. *I will not fail the Lord again*! he thought.

Back at the boat, Andrew and James manned the oars, pulling the boat through the water, while the others held the net taut. Peter splashed onto the beach to where Jesus sat by a small charcoal fire. Jesus had some bread and one small fish cooking. Jesus said to Peter, "Bring some of the fish you have just caught. Add them to mine, and we'll have breakfast together." So Peter waded out into the shallow water. In his exuberance, he grabbed a rope holding the net and dragged the net full of fish through the shallow water onto the shore.

As his disciples disembarked, Jesus called, "Come and have breakfast!"

Their doubts, their questions faded away as Jesus broke bread and handed it to each of them. Together they had breakfast. During the three years they had spent with Jesus, it had been his custom to instruct them in his kingdom as they sat digesting their food. But this time, Jesus asked a question. He turned to Simon Peter to ask, "Simon, do you love me?"

"Yes, Lord, you know I am fond of you."

"Feed my lambs," Jesus said to him.

Then Jesus asked a second time, "Simon, do you truly love me?"

Peter was grieved that the Lord had to ask him a second time. But again he answered, "Lord, you know that I care for you."

"Take care of my sheep," said Jesus.

Then Jesus asked the same question of Peter, this time using the same term of affection that Peter had used. "Simon, do you care for me?"

Peter was hurt, because Jesus had asked him three times, just as he had denied the Lord three times. But Peter could not keep sin in his heart. He answered, "Lord, you know all things. You know I love you."

"Feed my sheep," Jesus said, putting his hand on Peter's shoulder. There was forgiveness in his smile and resoluteness in his eyes. Jesus had named the man Peter, and on this rock he *would* build his church.

"When you were younger," Jesus said, "you dressed yourself and went wherever you wanted to go. But when you grow old, you will stretch out your hands and someone else will dress you. Things will change."

Peter looked into the eyes of his master as Jesus said, "By this I mean they will nail you to a cross, and that is how you will die. And by your death you will glorify God."

Peter heard these sobering words, but he would stand firm in his faith. Jesus was giving him a second chance.

CHAPTER **5 4**

Several weeks later, the eleven gathered again in the upper room.

"I look forward to seeing Jesus again," Thomas told the others.

"Do you think he will appear today?" John asked.

Then Jesus was standing there. "Peace be with you, my friends," he blessed them, then sat down to eat with them. When they finished the meal, Jesus gave his disciples a new command.

"Do not leave Jerusalem," he said, "but stay in the city until you have been clothed with power from on high. For John baptized with water, but in a few days you will be baptized with the Holy Spirit."

Then Jesus gave them a commission to go everywhere to persuade people to follow him and to enter the kingdom of God. It was late afternoon when they left the upper room. Jesus walked with them from Jerusalem toward Bethany and the Mount of Olives.

"Lord, will you restore Israel and establish your kingdom on earth at this time?" Andrew asked. After all, Jerusalem was still patrolled by Roman soldiers and the Jews still paid taxes to Rome.

Jesus didn't answer immediately but continued walking, passing over the Brook of Kidron and beginning the climb up Olivet. Near the summit, he turned to look on the city he loved—Jerusalem. Finally, Jesus answered, "It is not for you to know the time or seasons under God's authority or when he will return the kingdom of David to this land."

"What will happen to us?" Philip asked.

"You will go into all the world to preach the gospel," Jesus said. "You will be my witnesses to the ends of the earth."

Jesus lifted his hands to bless his disciples. Then slowly he began to lift off the ground, higher and higher, ascending to heaven.

Jesus ascended slowly, his hands still raised in blessing. No one spoke; no one took their eyes off Jesus.

Finally, a cloud blocked their vision, and John could no longer see him, yet he thought he knew what was happening at this moment. While the other apostles searched the sky for Jesus, young John looked into his heart to watch Jesus' return to heaven. He knew that the angels were greeting him with shouts of "Hallelujah!" and that the Father would arise from his throne to meet his beloved Son. John could almost hear God say, "Sit at my right hand, while I make your enemies your footstool."

The apostles stood a long time, staring up into the sky, watching and wondering. Then their thoughts were interrupted by two men in white who appeared beside them saying, "Men of Galilee, why do you stand gazing up at the sky? Has he not given you your commission? Return to Jerusalem. Tarry in prayer. The Holy Spirit will come on you, then preach with power the message of Jesus."

The apostles knew their time of instruction was over, and soon they must go to work. Soon they would go into all the world to preach the gospel with joy.

The heavenly messenger smiled on them and promised, "This same Jesus, who has been taken from you into heaven, will come again. In the same way you have seen him ascend into heaven, he shall return."

ABOUT THE AUTHOR

Elmer Leon Towns is co-founder, with Jerry Falwell, and vice-president of Liberty University, Lynchburg, Virginia. He is also dean of the School of Religion and dean of Liberty Baptist Theological Seminary at the University as well as teacher of the 2,000 member Pastor's Bible Sunday school class at Thomas Road Baptist Church. He is a Gold Medallion Award-winning author whose books include *The Names of the Holy Spirit, Fasting for Spiritual Breakthrough* and *The Prayer Journey Bible*. E. L. Towns and his wife, Ruth, have three grown children and ten grandchildren.

JESUS FROM GOD

Of all the words spoken by Jesus, listeners knew He was speaking as a man, while His message was from God.

Of all the ways Jesus related to people, they knew He was a man, while knowing He was from God.

Of all the people who saw Jesus, they thought of Him as a man, while realizing He was from God.

Of all the ways Jesus appeared to people, they accepted Him as a man, while understanding He was from God.

Of all the suffering Jesus endured on the cross, observers knew He was a man while seeing He was from God.

Of all the sinners who constantly gathered around Jesus, they knew He was a man while they accepted the fact He was from God.

Of all His weariness and limitations, His disciples knew He was a man while perceiving He was from God.

Elmer Towns

JESUS — GREATER THAN HIS ROOTS

Jesus was born in obscurity, not in the court of a king nor with the anticipation of royalty. He was cradled in a manger, surrounded by straw, some animals, and His father and mother. He was brought up in a country village, not in the synagogues of the religious, the palaces of the rich, nor the courts of the powerful. Jesus was trained at home by His mother, not the great universities of His day. He never crossed frontiers to see the sights, to interact with other cultures, or to broaden His experience. He was born of a people who were peculiarly secluded to their land, who had narrow religious customs, and had an exclusive monotheistic belief in God. He had no access to great philosophical literature of the Greeks, the great legal literature of the Romans, the mystical literature of the Persians, nor even to the great libraries of Jerusalem. He only had access to the scrolls of Scripture found in His small town synagogue. Yet, out of this limited environment and narrow heredity, stepped the one person who was peculiarly greater than His roots, who understood more than the learnings of the scholars, who had more authority than the political leaders, who had more might than the soldiers who carried their weapons of war. Out of this little town stepped a perfect man who changed the destination of history.

Elmer Towns

PERFECT—WITHOUT EXTREMES

Jesus was the perfect man without extremes, His zeal never degenerated into fanaticism, nor did His determination plunge into hard headedness. His love never became weakness, and His tenderness for people never became mere sentimentality. He was other-world minded, yet He was never detached from this world. He had dignity, yet was humble. He had self-respect, but was never proud. He was concerned about people, but did not have undue familiarity. He exercised self-denial in everything, yet was not self-effacing.

Jesus had the strength of manhood, yet the innocence of childhood. He was completely dedicated to doing God's will, yet He was devoted to helping people. He was uncompromisingly hard on sin yet tender in His love for the sinner. He never made a reputation for Himself, yet always stood in dignity that commanded the attention of others. He threw caution to the wind entering situations of danger and embarrassment, yet was always wise in His actions. Jesus was both unyieldingly firm yet sweet and gentle. He had the ruggedness of blue denim overalls, yet the elegance of fine lace.

Elmer Towns

HIS GREATNESS

The greatest man that has ever lived motivated the writing of some of the greatest books that influenced history, although He never wrote one.

The greatest man that has ever lived motivated the writing of some of the greatest music that has ever moved listeners, although He never composed a song.

The greatest man to ever live motivated His followers to build hospitals, orphanages, universities, and many other institutions to influence the world, although He never suggested them or built one Himself.

The greatest man to ever live had the greatest influence over the greatest number of individuals, although He seized no power by the sword, by political action, or by business manipulation.

The greatest man to ever live did the most good, for the most number of people, among the most number of ethnic groups, in the most diverse circumstances, that resulted in uplifting the most number of people, and giving them the best quality of life, and motivating them to share their blessing with the most needy recipients.

The story of the greatest man to ever live is told in the Bible, God's book. All God wants us to do is read it and believe it. The greatness of this character was in the simple way He lived, the simple sermon He preached and the simplicity of the way He helped people. The greatest man to ever live is Jesus who said, "Follow Me."

Elmer Towns